BIBLE
ACTIVITIES

Vickie Save

Illustrated by
Ken Save

BARBOUR BOOKS

An Imprint of Barbour Publishing, Inc.

©2000 by Barbour Publishing, Inc.

ISBN 1-57748-831-8

Published by Barbour Books, an imprint of Barbour Publishing, Inc., P.O. Box 719, Uhrichsville, Ohio 44683, www.barbourbooks.com

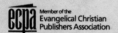 Member of the
Evangelical Christian
Publishers Association

Printed in the United States of America.
5 4 3

SUPER
BIBLE
ACTIVITIES

COLOR THE PICTURE

WHAT IS GRACE?

GOD'S WORD MAKES USE OF VERY HELPFUL TOOLS FOR TEACHING: *CONTRASTS.* THERE ARE CONTRASTS BETWEEN LIGHT AND DARKNESS, THE KINGDOM OF GOD AND THE KINGDOM OF SATAN, LIFE AND DEATH, LOST AND SAVED, AND *LAW AND GRACE.*

LAW AND GRACE ARE THE VERY HEART OF THE GOSPEL—THE DIFFERENCE BETWEEN THE TWO WILL DECIDE IF A PERSON IS SAVED AND HOW HE WILL LIVE THE CHRISTIAN LIFE.

IN ORDER TO UNDERSTAND WHAT GRACE REALLY IS, WE NEED TO KNOW WHAT THE LAW IS.

IN THIS BOOK, WE WILL LOOK AT BOTH OF THEM SO THAT WE MIGHT COMPLETELY UNDERSTAND *THE GRACE OF GOD.*

CROSS 'EM OUT

ON THE NEXT PAGE, CROSS OUT ALL THE
LETTERS THAT APPEAR IN THE BOX   FOUR
TIMES.   COMPLETE THE VERSE   BY PLACING
THE LETTERS THAT ARE LEFT OVER, AS THEY
APPEAR, IN THE SPACES PROVIDED.

```
H O F R L C I M T
D B T J G N Q A K
I P M V O H D P F
C R A K T E R V B
L S W H W V W G Q
Q P N W L B O C I
F G V D T R A N U
K A I Q M O H P L
M C N S G B K D F
```

"FOR THE LAW WAS GIVEN THROUGH MOSES; GRACE AND TRUTH CAME THROUGH ___ ___ ___ ___ ___ CHRIST."

JOHN 1:17

FILL in the BLANKS

USING THE WORDS BELOW, COMPLETE THE
VERSES ON THE NEXT PAGE.

BELIEVE   NECKS
PUTTING   GRACE
YOKE   SAVED
THEN   JESUS
GOD   ABLE
DISCIPLES   FATHERS

"NOW _____, WHY DO YOU TRY TO TEST _____ BY _____ ON THE _____ OF THE _____ A _____ THAT NEITHER WE NOR OUR _____ HAVE BEEN _____ TO BEAR? NO! WE _____ IT IS THROUGH THE _____ OF OUR LORD _____ THAT WE ARE _____, JUST AS THEY ARE."

ACTS 15:10–11

SCRAMBLED CIRCLES

ON THE NEXT PAGE, UNSCRAMBLE THE WORDS IN THE LIST BELOW. THEN USE THE CIRCLED LETTERS TO COMPLETE THE VERSE.

1. EMCA
2. SMEOS
3. VINGE
4. YTR
5. RTCSIH
6. KECSN
7. OYU
8. UJSES

1. ⭕ __ __ __
2. __ ⭕ __ __ __
3. __ __ __ __ ⭕
4. ⭕ __ __
5. __ __ __ ⭕ __ __
6. ⭕ __ __ __ __
7. __ __ ⭕
8. __ ⭕ __ __ __

"SO THEN, JUST AS YOU RECEIVED CHRIST JESUS AS LORD, __ __ __ __ __ __ __ __ TO LIVE IN HIM."

DOUBLE *the* FUN

UNSCRAMBLE THE UNDERLINED WORDS IN EACH VERSE. ON THE NEXT PAGE, PLACE YOUR ANSWERS IN THE SPACES PROVIDED AND THEN COMPLETE THE CROSSWORD PUZZLE.

1. "NOW IF THE <u>SNIYTIRM</u> THAT BROUGHT DEATH, WHICH WAS <u>REDNAVEG</u> IN LETTERS ON STONE, CAME WITH <u>OLRGY</u>, SO THAT THE ISRAELITES COULD NOT LOOK <u>DETLIASY</u> AT THE FACE OF MOSES BECAUSE OF ITS GLORY, FADING THOUGH IT WAS, WILL NOT THE MINISTRY OF THE SPIRIT BE EVEN MORE GLORIOUS?"

   2 CORINTHIANS 3:7–8

2. "IF THE MINISTRY THAT <u>NENSDCMO</u> MEN IS GLORIOUS, HOW MUCH <u>REMO</u> GLORIOUS IS THE MINISTRY THAT BRINGS RIGHTEOUSNESS!"

   2 CORINTHIANS 3:9

3. "<u>RFO</u> WHAT WAS GLORIOUS HAS NO GLORY NOW IN <u>ROIONMCPSA</u> WITH THE SURPASSING GLORY."

   2 CORINTHIANS 3:10

1. _____   _____

   _____   _____

2. _____   _____

3. _____   _____

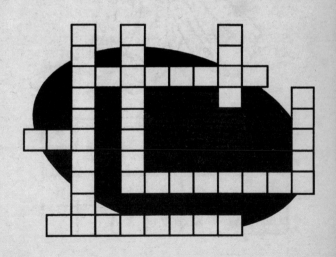

FINISH THE VERSE

USE THE CODE CHART BELOW TO FINISH THE VERSES ON THE NEXT PAGE. (EXAMPLE: K=24)

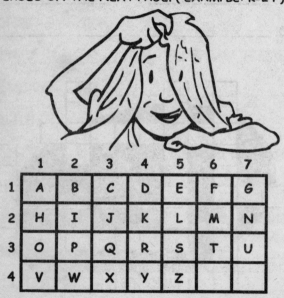

	1	2	3	4	5	6	7
1	A	B	C	D	E	F	G
2	H	I	J	K	L	M	N
3	O	P	Q	R	S	T	U
4	V	W	X	Y	Z		

"NOW THE __ __ __ IS THE
25 31 34 14
__ __ __ __ __ __, AND WHERE THE
35 32 22 34 22 36
SPIRIT OF THE LORD IS, THERE IS

__ __ __ __ __ __ __. AND WE, WHO
16 34 15 15 14 31 26
WITH UNVEILED __ __ __ __ __ ALL
16 11 13 15 35
__ __ __ __ __ __ __ THE LORD'S
34 15 16 25 15 13 36
__ __ __ __, ARE BEING
17 25 31 34 44
TRANSFORMED INTO HIS

__ __ __ __ __ __ __ __ WITH EVER-
25 22 24 15 27 15 35 35
INCREASING GLORY, WHICH

__ __ __ __ __ FROM THE
13 31 26 15 35
__ __ __ __, WHO IS THE SPIRIT."
25 31 34 14

2 CORINTHIANS 3:17–18

15

CROSS 'EM OUT

ON THE NEXT PAGE, CROSS OUT ALL THE
LETTERS THAT APPEAR IN THE BOX FOUR
TIMES. COMPLETE THE VERSE BY PLACING
THE LETTERS THAT ARE LEFT OVER, AS THEY
APPEAR, IN THE SPACES PROVIDED.

```
D  J  E  M  B  Q  L  P  E
N  C  U  I  O  K  G  W  S
K  S  P  V  X  D  S  N  V
O  R  F  L  M  V  F  C  J
F  G  Q  X  D  U  I  B  P
J  L  A  K  V  O  Q  M  C
N  U  M  C  S  X  L  T  G
B  E  O  I  U  K  Q  I  N
P  G  X  D  H  F  E  J  B
```

"BECAUSE OF THESE, THE __ __ __ __ __
OF GOD IS COMING."

COLOSSIANS 3:6

ASK YOURSELF

WHAT HAVE YOU LEARNED SO FAR? FIND OUT
BY ANSWERING THE QUESTIONS BELOW.

1. WHAT WAS GIVEN THROUGH
   MOSES?

   JOHN 1:17

   _____

2. WHAT CAME THROUGH JESUS
   CHRIST?

   JOHN 1:17

   _____

3. GOD MADE PAUL A COMPETENT
   MINISTER OF WHAT?

   2 CORINTHIANS 3:6

   _____

4. IS THE COVENANT OF THE LETTER OR OF THE SPIRIT?

2 CORINTHIANS 3:6

_____

5. WHAT DOES THE LETTER DO?

2 CORINTHIANS 3:6

_____

6. WHAT DOES THE SPIRIT DO?

2 CORINTHIANS 3:6

_____

COLOR THE PICTURE

A CLOSER LOOK AT THE LAW

THE BIBLE WILL SHOW US THAT THE LAW IS MADE UP OF THE *TEN COMMANDMENTS* AND THE CEREMONIAL LAWS GIVEN TO MOSES AT MOUNT SINAI.

THE GRACE OF JESUS CHRIST IS FAR GREATER THAN THE LAW THAT WAS GIVEN AT MOUNT SINAI. SO, WHY WAS THE LAW GIVEN?

THE LAW THAT GOD GAVE WAS FOR THE NATION OF ISRAEL SO THAT THEY WOULD PROSPER AND LIVE. WITH THE SACRIFICES THAT WERE NEEDED, IN THE LAW, THE PEOPLE OF ISRAEL WERE GIVEN A WAY OF HAVING THEIR SINS COVERED FOR A TIME.

BUT GOD HAS SOMETHING BETTER FOR YOU AND ME. THE ONLY PURPOSE FOR THE LAW TODAY IS A *SPIRITUAL* ONE—IT LEADS US TO JESUS CHRIST.

FILL in the BLANKS

USING THE WORDS BELOW, COMPLETE THE VERSES ON THE NEXT PAGE.

NATIONS   YOURSELVES
COVENANT   FULLY
EGYPT   POSSESSION
EAGLES'   CARRIED
BROUGHT   TREASURED

"'YOU _____ HAVE
SEEN WHAT I DID TO _____,
AND HOW I _____ YOU ON
_____ WINGS AND
_____ YOU TO MYSELF.
NOW IF YOU OBEY ME _____
AND KEEP MY _____, THEN
OUT OF ALL _____ YOU
WILL BE MY _____
_____.'"

CROSSWORD

ACROSS

1. "YOU SEE, AT JUST THE _____ TIME."
2. "WHEN WE WERE STILL _____."
3. "_____ DIED FOR THE UNGODLY."
4. "VERY RARELY WILL ANYONE DIE FOR A _____ MAN."

DOWN

1. "_____ FOR A GOOD MAN SOMEONE MIGHT POSSIBLY DARE TO DIE."
2. "BUT GOD _____ HIS OWN LOVE FOR US IN THIS."
3. "WHILE WE WERE STILL _____."
4. "CHRIST DIED FOR _____."

CROSS 'EM OUT

ON THE NEXT PAGE, CROSS OUT ALL THE
LETTERS THAT APPEAR IN THE BOX FOUR
TIMES. COMPLETE THE VERSE BY PLACING
THE LETTERS THAT ARE LEFT OVER, AS THEY
APPEAR, IN THE SPACES PROVIDED.

```
G  M  J  Q  H  O  D  I  P
R  C  F  W  K  Z  U  W  R
K  T  N  Z  P  B  J  Q  M
D  I  U  S  T  R  F  Z  W
O  B  H  C  Z  G  N  C  D
P  G  J  Q  F  W  J  L  O
T  N  F  U  P  H  A  U  T
V  C  O  R  M  N  G  I  B
K  I  E  H  D  B  M  K  Q
```

"WE KNOW THAT THE LAW IS SPIRITUAL;
BUT I AM UNSPIRITUAL, SOLD AS A
_ _ _ _ _ _ TO SIN."

ROMANS 7:14

SCRAMBLED CIRCLES

ON THE NEXT PAGE, UNSCRAMBLE THE WORDS IN THE LIST BELOW. THEN USE THE CIRCLED LETTERS TO COMPLETE THE VERSE.

1. LDSO

2. ERDA

3. IHRTCS

4. WLA

5. VATNOENC

6. LARYRE

7. GEELA

8. EDDI

1. _ _ _ ◯

2. _ _ _ ◯

3. ◯ _ _ _ _ _

4. ◯ _ _

5. _ _ _ _ _ ◯ _ _

6. _ _ ◯ _ _

7. ◯ _ _ _ _

8. _ _ _ ◯

"THEREFORE NO ONE WILL BE
_ _ _ _ _ _ _ _ _ RIGHTEOUS IN
HIS SIGHT BY OBSERVING THE LAW;
RATHER, THROUGH THE LAW WE BECOME
CONSCIOUS OF SIN."

ROMANS 3:20

FINISH THE VERSE

USE THE CODE CHART BELOW TO FINISH THE
VERSE ON THE NEXT PAGE. (EXAMPLE: K=24)

	1	2	3	4	5	6	7
1	A	B	C	D	E	F	G
2	H	I	J	K	L	M	N
3	O	P	Q	R	S	T	U
4	V	W	X	Y	Z		

"IF YOU __ __ __ __ __ OBEY THE
16 37 25 25 44

LORD YOUR __ __ __ AND CAREFULLY
17 31 14

__ __ __ __ __ __ ALL HIS
16 31 25 25 31 42

__ __ __ __ __ __ __ __ I GIVE YOU
13 31 26 26 11 27 14 35

TODAY, THE __ __ __ __ YOUR GOD
25 31 34 14

WILL SET YOU __ __ __ __ ABOVE
21 22 17 21

ALL THE __ __ __ __ __ __ __ ON
27 11 36 22 31 27 35

EARTH."

DEUTERONOMY 28:1

SCRAMBLED VERSES

UNSCRAMBLE THE WORDS BELOW AND
COMPLETE THE VERSE ON THE NEXT PAGE.

"WVEHOER, FI UYO OD TNO EYBO
HET RLDO UROY DGO DAN OD TON
EUAYLRLCF OLFWLO LAL SHI
AOCMNDMS NAD RSEECDE I MA
NIGVGI UOY YTAOD, LAL EEHST
SRESCU ILWL ECMO OUNP OYU ADN
AERTOVEK UYO."

"_____, _____

____ ____ _____ _____

_____ ____ ____ _____ ____

____ ____ _____

_____ _____ ____ ____

_____ _____

_____ ____ ____

_____ _____ _____,

_____ _____ _____

____ _____ ____ ____ ____

____ _____ ____."

DEUTERONOMY 28:15

SECRET CODES

TO SOLVE THE CODED VERSE BELOW, LOOK AT EACH LETTER AND WRITE THE ONE THAT COMES BEFORE IT IN THE ALPHABET.

"XIBU, UIFO, XBT UIF QVSQPTF PG UIF MBX? JU XBT BEEFE CFDBVTF PG USBOTHSFTTJPOT VOUJM UIF TFFE UP XIPN UIF QSPNJTF SFGFSSF IBE DPNF. UIF MBX XBT QVU JOUP FGGFDU UISPVHI BOHFMT CZ B NFEJBUPS."

A B C D E F G H I J K L M N O P Q R S T U V W X Y Z

"_____, _____, _____

_____ _____ ____

_____ _____ ?

_____ _____ ____

_____

_____ ____ _____

_____ ____ _____

_____ _____

____ _____ _____.

_____ _____

_____ _____ ____

_____ ____ ____

_____."

GALATIANS 3:19

35

DOUBLE *the* FUN

UNSCRAMBLE THE UNDERLINED WORDS IN
EACH VERSE. ON THE NEXT PAGE, PLACE YOUR
ANSWERS IN THE SPACES PROVIDED AND
THEN COMPLETE THE CROSSWORD PUZZLE.

1. "SO THEN, THE LAW IS <u>LOYH</u>, AND THE
   <u>MDNEACMNTOM</u> IS HOLY, <u>TGSOIRUHE</u>
   AND <u>ODGO</u>."

   ROMANS 7:12

2. "WE KNOW THAT THE LAW IS <u>IARLSIUTP</u>;
   BUT I AM <u>RSUATILPNUI</u>, SOLD AS A
   <u>EVLSA</u> TO <u>NSI</u>."

   ROMANS 7:14

36

ASK YOURSELF

WHAT HAVE YOU LEARNED SO FAR? FIND OUT
BY ANSWERING THE QUESTIONS BELOW.

1. WHAT DID MOSES WRITE DOWN?

    EXODUS 24:4–8

    _____

2. HOW LONG WAS THE LAW TO BE IN
    EFFECT FOR ISRAEL?

    GALATIANS 3:19

    _____

3. WHAT DO YOU THINK THE SEED
    REFERS TO?

    GALATIANS 3:19

    _____

4. HOW DOES PAUL DESCRIBE THE LAW?

ROMANS 7:12–14

_____

5. IS THE LAW SPIRITUAL OR PHYSICAL?

ROMANS 7:12–14

_____

6. DOES THE LAW HAVE A SPIRITUAL PURPOSE IN OUR LIVES?

ROMANS 3:20

_____

COLOR THE PICTURE

THE PURPOSE OF THE LAW

THE LAW DOES HAVE A PURPOSE—IT IS A SPIRITUAL PURPOSE.

THE PURPOSE IS FOUND IN THE QUESTION, "WHO TURNS TO JESUS CHRIST FOR SALVATION?" ONLY THOSE WHO KNOW THEY NEED TO BE SAVED.

THE LAW IS LIKE A TEACHER. IT TEACHES US THE DIFFERENCE BETWEEN RIGHT AND WRONG; IT TEACHES US ABOUT ACTIONS AND THOUGHTS AND ATTITUDES THAT ARE SEEN AS SIN IN GOD'S EYES. IT HELPS US TO UNDERSTAND THE PERFECT REQUIREMENTS OF GOD FOR HOLINESS AND RIGHTEOUSNESS.

BUT *THIS PERFECTION* WE CAN NEVER MEET.

CROSS 'EM OUT

ON THE NEXT PAGE, CROSS OUT ALL THE LETTERS THAT APPEAR IN THE BOX FOUR TIMES. COMPLETE THE VERSE BY PLACING THE LETTERS THAT ARE LEFT OVER, AS THEY APPEAR, IN THE SPACES PROVIDED.

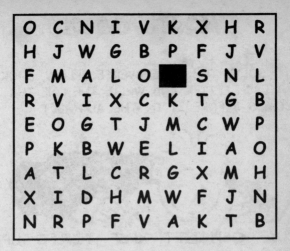

O	C	N	I	V	K	X	H	R
H	J	W	G	B	P	F	J	V
F	M	A	L	O	■	S	N	L
R	V	I	X	C	K	T	G	B
E	O	G	T	J	M	C	W	P
P	K	B	W	E	L	I	A	O
A	T	L	C	R	G	X	M	H
X	I	D	H	M	W	F	J	N
N	R	P	F	V	A	K	T	B

"WHAT, THEN, WAS THE PURPOSE OF THE
LAW? IT WAS ADDED BECAUSE
OF TRANSGRESSIONS UNTIL THE
___ ___ ___ ___ TO WHOM THE PROMISE
REFERRED HAD COME."

GALATIANS 3:19

43

SECRET CODES

TO SOLVE THE CODED VERSE BELOW, LOOK AT EACH LETTER AND WRITE THE ONE THAT COMES BEFORE IT IN THE ALPHABET.

"UIF QSPNJTFT XFSF TQPLFO UP BCSBIBN BOE UP IJT TFFE. UIF TDSJQUVSF EPFT OPU TBZ 'BOE UP TFFET,' NFBOJOH NBOZ QFPQMF, CVU 'BOE UP ZPVS TFFT,' NFBOJOH POF QFSTPO, XIP JT DISJTU."

ABCDEFGHIJKLMNOPQRST
UVWXYZ

"_____ _____

_____ _____ _____

_____ _____ _____

_____ _____. _____

_____ _____

_____,_____ _____

_____ _____, _____

_____ _____ _____

_____ _____,_____

_____ _____, _____

_____ _____."

GALATIANS 3:16

DOUBLE the FUN

UNSCRAMBLE THE UNDERLINED WORDS IN THE VERSES. ON THE NEXT PAGE, PLACE YOUR ANSWERS IN THE SPACES PROVIDED AND THEN COMPLETE THE CROSSWORD PUZZLE.

"THE LAW WAS <u>DAEDD</u> SO THAT THE <u>PERSATSS</u> MIGHT <u>REESNICA</u>. BUT WHERE SIN INCREASED, GRACE INCREASED ALL THE MORE, SO THAT, JUST AS SIN REIGNED IN DEATH, SO ALSO GRACE MIGHT REIGN THROUGH <u>GSETIRSUEHSNO</u> TO BRING <u>EAELRNT</u> LIFE THROUGH JESUS <u>IRSTHC</u> OUR LORD."

ROMANS 5:20–21

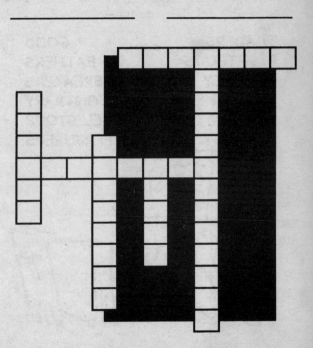

FILL in the BLANKS

USING THE WORDS BELOW, COMPLETE THE
VERSES ON THE NEXT PAGE.

TRADERS

RIGHTEOUS

UNGODLY

DOCTRINE

LAW

PROPERLY

GOOD

FATHERS

LAWBREAKERS

CONTRARY

IRRELIGIOUS

PERJURERS

"WE KNOW THAT THE LAW IS _____ IF ONE USES IT _____. WE ALSO KNOW THAT _____ IS MADE NOT FOR THE _____ BUT FOR _____ AND REBELS, THE _____ AND SINFUL, THE UNHOLY AND _____; FOR THOSE WHO KILL THEIR _____ OR MOTHERS, FOR MURDERERS, FOR ADULTERERS AND PERVERTS, FOR SLAVE _____ AND LIARS AND _____—AND FOR WHATEVER ELSE IS _____ TO THE SOUND _____."

1 TIMOTHY 1:8-10

FINISH THE VERSE

USE THE CODE CHART BELOW TO FINISH THE VERSE ON THE NEXT PAGE. (EXAMPLE: K=24)

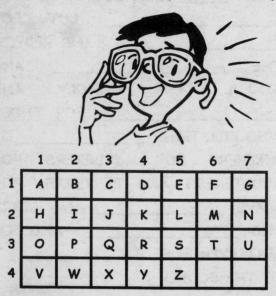

	1	2	3	4	5	6	7
1	A	B	C	D	E	F	G
2	H	I	J	K	L	M	N
3	O	P	Q	R	S	T	U
4	V	W	X	Y	Z		

"_____ NO ONE
36 21 15 34 15 16 31 34 15

WILL BE _____
14 15 13 25 11 34 15 14

_____ IN HIS
34 22 17 21 36 15 31 37 35

SIGHT BY _____
31 12 35 15 34 41 22 27 17

THE LAW; _____,
34 11 36 21 15 34

THROUGH THE ___ WE BECOME
25 11 42

_____ OF
13 31 27 35 13 22 31 37 35

___."
35 22 27

ROMANS 3:20

51

SCRAMBLED VERSES

UNSCRAMBLE THE WORDS BELOW AND COMPLETE THE VERSE ON THE NEXT PAGE.

"RFOEEHTER, STJU SA NSI EDTEREN HET LODWR GTOHUHR EON NMA, DAN TEHAD RHUTGOH INS, NAD NI STHI AYW AHDET MEAC OT LAL NME, SCBEAEU LAL DISNEN—RFO FEORBE ETH WLA SWA VNGEI, ISN ASW NI EHT LODRO."

52

"_____, _____
_____ _____
_____ _____ _____
_____ _____, _____
_____, _____
_____ _____
_____ _____ _____
_____ _____, _____
_____ _____ —_____
_____ _____ _____
_____ _____, _____
_____ _____ _____
_____."

ROMANS 5:12-13

DOUBLE the FUN

UNSCRAMBLE THE UNDERLINED WORDS IN EACH VERSE. ON THE NEXT PAGE, PLACE YOUR ANSWERS IN THE SPACES PROVIDED AND THEN COMPLETE THE CROSSWORD PUZZLE.

1. "WHAT SHALL WE SAY, ENHT? IS THE LAW SIN? NTECAYLIR NOT! INDEED I WOULD NOT HAVE KNOWN WHAT SIN WAS EXCEPT THROUGH THE LAW. FOR I WOULD NOT EHVA KNOWN WHAT NVCOTIGE REALLY WAS IF THE LAW HAD NOT SAID, 'DO NOT COVET.'"

   ROMANS 7:7

2. "BUT SIN, IESZGNI THE OPPORTUNITY AFFORDED BY THE COMMANDMENT, PRODUCED IN ME EVERY KIND OF OOVCTSUE RESEID. FOR APART FROM LAW, NSI IS DEAD."

   ROMANS 7:8

1. _____   _____

   _____   _____

2. _____   _____

   _____   _____

FILL in the BLANKS

USING THE WORDS BELOW, COMPLETE THE
VERSES ON THE NEXT PAGE.

LIFE	ONCE
ALIVE	APART
COMMANDMENT	ACTUALLY
SPRANG	DEATH
INTENDED	FOUND
DIED	LIFE

"_____ I WAS _____

_____ FROM LAW; BUT WHEN

THE _____ CAME,

SIN _____ TO _____ AND

I _____. I _____ THAT THE

VERY COMMANDMENT THAT WAS

_____ TO BRING _____

_____ BROUGHT

_____."

ROMANS 7:9-10

SECRET CODES

TO SOLVE THE CODED VERSES BELOW, LOOK AT EACH LETTER AND WRITE THE ONE THAT COMES BEFORE IT IN THE ALPHABET.

"GPS TJO, TFJZJOH UIF PQQPSUVOJUZ BGGPSEFE CZ UIF DPNNBOENFOU, EFDFJWFE NF, BOE UISPVHI UIF DPNNBOENFOU QVU NF UP EFBUI. TP UIFO, UIF MBX JT IPMZ, BOE UIF DPNNBOENFOU JT IPMZ, SJHIUFPVT BOE HPPE."

A B C D E F G H I J K L M N O P Q R S T
U V W X Y Z

" _____ _____ , _____ Z _____

_____ _____ _____

_____ _____ _____

_____ _____ _____ ,

_____ _____ _____ , _____

_____ _____ _____

_____ _____ _____ .

_____ , _____ _____ _____

_____ , _____ _____

_____ , _____ _____

_____ _____ _____ ."

ROMANS 7:11-12

59

SCRAMBLED CIRCLES

ON THE NEXT PAGE, UNSCRAMBLE THE WORDS IN THE LIST BELOW. THEN USE THE CIRCLED LETTERS TO COMPLETE THE VERSE.

1. EBRO

2. LTUTRYE

3. VCEEEDI

4. DGOO

5. NESMA

6. IFLE

1. _ _ ◯ _

2. _ _ _ ◯ _ _ _

3. _ _ ◯ _ _ _ _

4. _ ◯ _ _

5. ◯ _ _ _ _

6. _ _ _ ◯

"DID THAT WHICH IS GOOD, THEN,
_ _ _ _ _ _ DEATH TO ME?
BY NO MEANS."

ROMANS 7:13

CROSSWORD

ACROSS

1. "BUT THE SCRIPTURE DECLARES THAT THE WHOLE WORLD IS A _____ OF SIN."
2. "SO THAT WHAT WAS _____."
3. "BEING GIVEN THROUGH FAITH IN _____ CHRIST."
4. "MIGHT BE GIVEN TO THOSE _____ BELIEVE."

DOWN

1. " BEFORE THIS FAITH CAME, WE WERE HELD _____ BY THE LAW."
2. "LOCKED UP UNTIL _____ SHOULD BE REVEALED."
3. "SO THE LAW WAS PUT IN _____ TO LEAD US TO CHRIST."
4. "THAT ___ MIGHT BE JUSTIFIED BY FAITH."

ASK YOURSELF

WHAT HAVE YOU LEARNED SO FAR? FIND OUT
BY ANSWERING THE QUESTIONS BELOW.

1. WHAT DOES THE SCRIPTURE SAY
   ABOUT THE WHOLE WORLD?

   GALATIANS 3:22–24

   _____

2. HOW IS THE PROMISE GIVEN?

   GALATIANS 3:22–24

   _____

3. WHO CAN RECEIVE THIS PROMISE?

   GALATIANS 3:22–24

   _____

4. WHAT HOLDS US PRISONER TO OUR SIN?

GALATIANS 3:22–24

_____

5. HOW LONG WOULD THE LAW KEEP US LOCKED UP?

GALATIANS 3:22–24

_____

6. WHY WAS THE LAW PUT IN CHARGE TO LEAD US TO CHRIST?

GALATIANS 3:22–24

_____

COLOR THE PICTURE

THE LAW IS POWERLESS...

THE LAW IS LIKE A MIRROR. IT CAN SHOW US THAT OUR FACES ARE DIRTY, BUT IT CAN'T WASH THEM FOR US.

THIS IS ALL GOD WANTED THE LAW TO DO. IT SHOWS US THAT WE ARE *DEAD IN OUR SINS* AND IN NEED OF *LIFE*, BUT IT IS POWERLESS TO DO ANYTHING OTHER THAN THAT.

THE LAW CANNOT GIVE LIFE—IF IT COULD, THEN WOULD THERE HAVE BEEN ANY NEED FOR JESUS TO COME? IF THE LAW COULD HAVE MADE ANYONE PERFECT OR GIVEN ANYONE LIFE, THEN JESUS' SACRIFICE FOR US WOULD HAVE BEEN FOR NOTHING.

ONLY JESUS CHRIST CAN GIVE LIFE!

DOUBLE the FUN

UNSCRAMBLE THE UNDERLINED WORDS IN EACH VERSE. ON THE NEXT PAGE, PLACE YOUR ANSWERS IN THE SPACES PROVIDED AND THEN COMPLETE THE CROSSWORD PUZZLE.

1. "THE MFORRE GAONTEULIR IS SET DSIAE BECAUSE IT WAS WEAK AND USELESS."

HEBREWS 7:18

2. "(FOR THE WLA MADE NOTHING EFTCRPE), AND A BTERTE HOPE IS DTEDOINRCU, BY WHICH WE WRDA NEAR TO GOD."

HEBREWS 7:19

1. _____ _____

   _____

2. _____ _____

   _____

   _____

CROSS 'EM OUT

ON THE NEXT PAGE, CROSS OUT ALL THE
LETTERS THAT APPEAR IN THE BOX FOUR
TIMES. COMPLETE THE VERSE BY PLACING
THE LETTERS THAT ARE LEFT OVER, AS THEY
APPEAR, IN THE SPACES PROVIDED.

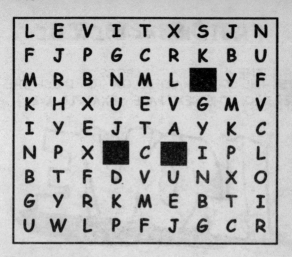

"THE LAW IS ONLY A __ __ __ __ __ __
OF THE GOOD THINGS THAT ARE COMING
—NOT THE REALITIES THEMSELVES."

HEBREWS 10:1

FINISH THE VERSE

USE THE CODE CHART BELOW TO FINISH THE VERSE ON THE NEXT PAGE. (EXAMPLE: K=24)

	1	2	3	4	5	6	7
1	A	B	C	D	E	F	G
2	H	I	J	K	L	M	N
3	O	P	Q	R	S	T	U
4	V	W	X	Y	Z		

"FOR WHAT THE LAW WAS

_____ _____ _____ _____ _____ _____ _____ _____ _____ TO DO IN
32 31 42 15 34 25 15 35 35

THAT IT WAS _____ _____ _____ _____ _____ _____ _____ _____
42 15 11 24 15 27 15 14

BY THE SINFUL _____ _____ _____ _____ _____ _____,
27 11 36 37 34 15

_____ _____ _____ DID BY SENDING HIS OWN
17 31 14

_____ _____ _____ IN THE LIKENESS OF
35 31 27

_____ _____ _____ _____ _____ _____ MAN TO BE A SIN
35 22 27 16 37 25

_____ _____ _____ _____ _____ _____ _____ _____. AND SO HE
31 16 16 15 34 22 27 17

CONDEMNED _____ _____ _____ IN SINFUL
35 22 27

MAN."

ROMANS 8:3

SCRAMBLED VERSES

UNSCRAMBLE THE WORDS BELOW AND COMPLETE THE VERSE ON THE NEXT PAGE.

"SI ETH WLA, ORHTEREFE, SPOOEDP OT HET SMRPIESO FO DGO? TOBALLYEUS OTN! RFO FI A WAL AHD NBEE EGNVI ATHT UCODL RPIMAT FELI, NHET NEGRTSEUHISOS LODUW AECTNYLIR AHVE CEOM YB ETH AWL."

"_____ _____ _____,

_____, _____

___ ___ _____

___ _____ ? _____

___ ! ___ ___ _____ _____

_____ _____ ___ _____

_____ _____ ___ _____

_____, _____ _____ -

_____ ___ _____ _____

___ ___ _____ ___ ___ _____

_____ ."

GALATIANS 3:21

SCRAMBLED CIRCLES

ON THE NEXT PAGE, UNSCRAMBLE THE WORDS IN THE LIST BELOW. THEN USE THE CIRCLED LETTERS TO COMPLETE THE VERSE.

1. ETJUIDISF

2. WLA

3. LILW

4. CIRTSH

5. UHTOHGR

1. _ _ _ _ _ ◯ _ _ _

2. _ ◯ _

3. _ ◯ _ _

4. _ _ _ _ _ ◯

5. _ ◯ _ _ _ _

"KNOW THAT A MAN IS NOT JUSTIFIED
BY OBSERVING THE LAW, BUT BY
__ __ __ __ __ IN JESUS CHRIST."

GALATIANS 2:16

SECRET CODES

TO SOLVE THE CODED VERSES BELOW, LOOK AT EACH LETTER AND WRITE THE ONE THAT COMES BEFORE IT IN THE ALPHABET.

"CVU CFDBVTF PG IJT HSFBU MPWF GPS VT, HPE, XIP JT SJDI JO NFSDZ, NBEF VT BMJWF XJUI DISJTU FWFO XIFO XF XFSF EFBE JO USBOTHSFTTJPOT—JU JT CZ HSBDF ZPV IBWF CFFO TBWFE."

A B C D E F G H I J K L M N O P Q R S T
U V W X Y Z

"_____ _____ ____

_____ _____ _____

_____ ____, _____, _____

____ _____ _____,

____ _____ ____

_____ _____ ____

____ _____ _____

____ _____ -

____ _____ ____

____ _____ ____

_____."

EPHESIANS 2:4–5

ASK YOURSELF

WHAT HAVE YOU LEARNED SO FAR? FIND OUT
BY ANSWERING THE QUESTIONS BELOW.

1. WHAT HAS HAPPENED TO THE LAW
   FOR TODAY?
   HEBREWS 7:18-19

   _____

2. CAN A PERSON BE JUSTIFIED BY
   KEEPING THE LAW?
   GALATIANS 2:16

   _____

3. HOW THEN ARE WE JUSTIFIED?
   GALATIANS 2:16

   _____

4. DOES THE LAW HAVE THE ABILITY TO GIVE US LIFE?

ROMANS 7:10

_____

5. WHAT DOES THE LAW BRING?

ROMANS 7:10

_____

6. WHO MADE US ALIVE WITH CHRIST?

EPHESIANS 2:4–5

_____

COLOR THE PICTURE

CHRIST FULFILLED THE LAW

JESUS DID NOT COME TO ABOLISH THE LAW—
HE CAME TO *FULFILL* IT. EVERY REQUIREMENT
THAT THE LAW DEMANDED, JESUS MET, AND
HE MET IT PERFECTLY. HE LIVED A
COMPLETELY SINLESS LIFE; HE WALKED IN
PERFECT LOVE.

HIS DEATH ON THE CROSS PAID IN FULL THE
WAGES OF SIN FOR THE ENTIRE WORLD.

JESUS CHRIST DID IT ALL—FOR US!

GOD NAILED THE LAW TO THE CROSS; HE WAS
COMPLETELY SATISFIED WITH THE SACRIFICE
THAT HIS SON MADE ON OUR BEHALF.

IT IS GOD'S DESIRE THAT THE LAW REMAIN
NAILED TO THAT CROSS!

CROSSWORD

ACROSS

1. "'DO NOT _____ THAT I HAVE COME.'"
2. "'TO _____ THE LAW OR THE PROPHETS.'"
3. "'I HAVE NOT COME TO ABOLISH _____.'"
4. "'BUT TO FULFILL _____.'"

DOWN

1. "'I TELL YOU THE TRUTH, UNTIL HEAVEN AND EARTH _____.'"
2. "'NOT THE SMALLEST _____, NOT THE LEAST STROKE OF A PEN.'"
3. "'WILL BY ANY _____ DISAPPEAR FROM THE LAW.'"
4. "'_____ EVERYTHING IS ACCOMPLISHED.'"

SCRAMBLED VERSES

UNSCRAMBLE THE WORDS BELOW AND COMPLETE THE VERSE ON THE NEXT PAGE.

"EH IDSA OT METH, 'HIST SI HATW I ODLT UYO IHELW I WSA LITSL TWIH UYO: IYVETGNHRE UTMS EB LLUFLDEIF AHTT SI TEWNIRT OATUB EM IN HET LWA FO OESSM, ETH SPRPHTEO DAN HET MASLPS.'"

86

"_____ _____ _____ _____ _____,
_____ _____ _____ _____ _____
_____ _____ _____ _____ _____
_____ : _____ _____
_____ _____ _____
_____ _____ _____
_____ _____ _____ _____
_____ _____ _____ _____,
_____ _____ _____ _____
_____ _____ ."

LUKE 24:44

CROSS 'EM OUT

ON THE NEXT PAGE, CROSS OUT ALL THE LETTERS THAT APPEAR IN THE BOX FOUR TIMES. COMPLETE THE VERSE BY PLACING THE LETTERS THAT ARE LEFT OVER, AS THEY APPEAR, IN THE SPACES PROVIDED.

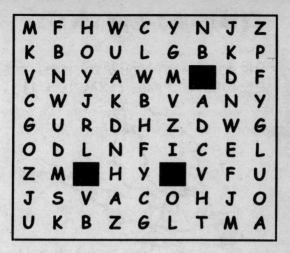

M	F	H	W	C	Y	N	J	Z
K	B	O	U	L	G	B	K	P
V	N	Y	A	W	M	█	D	F
C	W	J	K	B	V	A	N	Y
G	U	R	D	H	Z	D	W	G
O	D	L	N	F	I	C	E	L
Z	M	█	H	Y	█	V	F	U
J	S	V	A	C	O	H	J	O
U	K	B	Z	G	L	T	M	A

"FOR WE DO NOT HAVE A HIGH
___ ___ ___ ___ ___ ___ WHO IS UNABLE
TO SYMPATHIZE WITH OUR
WEAKNESSES."

HEBREWS 4:15

89

FINISH THE VERSE

USE THE CODE CHART BELOW TO FINISH THE
VERSE ON THE NEXT PAGE. (EXAMPLE: K=24)

	1	2	3	4	5	6	7
1	A	B	C	D	E	F	G
2	H	I	J	K	L	M	N
3	O	P	Q	R	S	T	U
4	V	W	X	Y	Z		

"FOR THE _____ _____ _____ _____ _____ OF _____ _____ _____
        42   11   17   15   35   35   22   27

IS _____ _____ _____ _____ _____,   BUT   THE
   14   15   11   36   21

_____ _____ _____ _____ OF _____ _____ _____ IS
17   22   16   36   17   31   14

_____ _____ _____ _____ _____ _____ _____   _____ _____ _____ _____
15   36   15   34   27   11   25   25   22   16   15

IN   CHRIST   _____ _____ _____ _____ _____   OUR
              23   15   35   37   35

_____ _____ _____ _____."
25   31   34   14

ROMANS 6:23

91

SCRAMBLED CIRCLES

ON THE NEXT PAGE, UNSCRAMBLE THE WORDS IN THE LIST BELOW. THEN USE THE CIRCLED LETTERS TO COMPLETE THE VERSE.

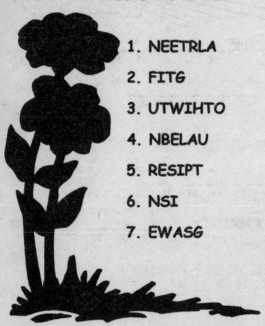

1. NEETRLA

2. FITG

3. UTWIHTO

4. NBELAU

5. RESIPT

6. NSI

7. EWASG

1. _ _ _ _ _ _ ◯ _

2. _ _ _ _ ◯ _

3. _ _ _ _ ◯ _ _

4. _ ◯ _ _ _ _

5. _ _ ◯ _ _ _

6. _ _ ◯ _

7. _ _ ◯ _ _

"HE IS THE _ _ _ _ _ _ _
SACRIFICE FOR OUR SINS, AND NOT
ONLY FOR OURS BUT ALSO FOR THE SINS
OF THE WHOLE WORLD."

1 JOHN 2:2

FILL in the BLANKS

USING THE WORDS BELOW, COMPLETE THE
VERSES ON THE NEXT PAGE.

WRITTEN	NATURE
REGULATIONS	DEAD
SINS	NAILING
UNCIRCUMCISION	CROSS
FORGAVE	OPPOSED

"WHEN YOU WERE _____ IN YOUR

_____ AND IN THE

_____ OF

YOUR SINFUL _____, GOD

MADE YOU ALIVE WITH CHRIST. HE

_____ US ALL OUR

SINS, HAVING CANCELED THE

_____ CODE, WITH ITS

_____, THAT WAS

AGAINST US AND THAT STOOD

_____ TO US; HE TOOK IT

AWAY, _____ IT TO THE

_____."

COLOSSIANS 2:13–14

95

DOUBLE the FUN

UNSCRAMBLE THE UNDERLINED WORDS IN EACH VERSE. ON THE NEXT PAGE, PLACE YOUR ANSWERS IN THE SPACES PROVIDED AND THEN COMPLETE THE CROSSWORD PUZZLE.

1. "FOR WHAT THE LAW WAS <u>LOWESEPRS</u> TO DO IN THAT IT WAS <u>NKEWEDEA</u> BY THE SINFUL NATURE, GOD DID BY <u>NNSDGIE</u> HIS OWN SON IN THE LIKENESS OF <u>NLUSFI</u> MAN TO BE A SIN OFFERING."

ROMANS 8:3

2. "AND SO HE <u>MODNDCEEN</u> SIN IN SINFUL MAN, IN ORDER THAT THE RIGHTEOUS REQUIREMENTS OF THE LAW MIGHT BE FULLY MET IN US, WHO <u>OD</u> NOT <u>ILEV</u> ACCORDING TO THE SINFUL NATURE BUT ACCORDING TO THE <u>IRISTP</u>."

ROMANS 8:3-4

1. _____ _____

_____ _____

2. _____ _____

_____ _____

ASK YOURSELF

WHAT HAVE YOU LEARNED SO FAR? FIND OUT
BY ANSWERING THE QUESTIONS BELOW.

1. WHAT DID CHRIST COME TO DO
CONCERNING THE LAW?

MATTHEW 5:17–18

_____

2. WHO DID JESUS SAY WOULD
FULFILL THE LAW?

MATTHEW 5:17–18

_____

3. WHAT DID CHRIST DO WITH THE
WRITTEN CODE?

COLOSSIANS 2:13–14

_____

CANCELLED

4. ONCE THE LAW WAS CANCELLED, WHAT DID JESUS DO WITH IT?

COLOSSIANS 2:13–14

_____

5. THEREFORE, WHERE SHOULD THE LAW REMAIN?

COLOSSIANS 2:14

_____

6. SINCE JESUS FULFILLED THE LAW, DOES IT MAKE ANY SENSE FOR US TO TRY TO FULFILL IT?

GALATIANS 3:1–3

_____

COLOR *THE* PICTURE

CHRIST SET US FREE FROM THE LAW

WE WERE BORN INTO THIS WORLD AS SLAVES TO SIN. WE WERE BORN SPIRITUALLY *DEAD*.

BY THE LAW, WE WERE HELD PRISONER TO OUR SINFULNESS. FOR US TO BE SET FREE, A PRICE HAD TO BE PAID. THE PRICE THAT THE LAW REQUIRED WAS THE *PRECIOUS BLOOD OF JESUS*—NOTHING ELSE WOULD DO.

AT THE RIGHT TIME, GOD SENT HIS SON, JESUS, INTO THE WORLD TO PAY THE PRICE THAT THE LAW DEMANDED. JESUS REDEEMED US FROM THE LAW OF SIN AND DEATH.

HE DID THIS, NOT TO KEEP US AS SLAVES, BUT TO SET US FREE—TO MAKE US HIS SONS AND DAUGHTERS AND TO GIVE US THE FULL RIGHT TO BECOME *CHILDREN OF GOD*.

FILL in the BLANKS

USING THE WORDS BELOW, COMPLETE THE VERSE ON THE NEXT PAGE.

TREE

REDEEMED

CURSED

EVERYONE

CHRIST

CURSE

HUNG

BECOMING

LAW

WRITTEN

"_____ _____ US FROM THE _____ OF THE _____ BY _____ A CURSE FOR US, FOR IT IS _____: '_____ IS _____ WHO IS _____ ON A _____.'"

GALATIANS 3:13

103

FINISH THE VERSE

USE THE CODE CHART BELOW TO FINISH THE
VERSES ON THE NEXT PAGE. (EXAMPLE: K=24)

	1	2	3	4	5	6	7
1	A	B	C	D	E	F	G
2	H	I	J	K	L	M	N
3	O	P	Q	R	S	T	U
4	V	W	X	Y	Z		

"FOR YOU __ __ __ __ THAT
24 27 31 42

IT WAS NOT WITH

__ __ __ __ __ __ __ __ __ __
32 15 34 22 35 21 11 12 25 15

THINGS SUCH AS __ __ __ __ __ __
35 22 25 41 15 34

OR __ __ __ __ THAT YOU WERE
17 31 25 14

REDEEMED FROM THE __ __ __ __ __
15 26 32 36 44

WAY OF __ __ __ __ HANDED DOWN
25 22 16 15

TO YOU FROM YOUR

__ __ __ __ __ __ __ __ __ __ ,
16 31 34 15 16 11 36 21 15 34 35

BUT WITH THE __ __ __ __ __ __ __ __
32 34 15 13 22 31 37 35

BLOOD OF CHRIST, A __ __ __ __
25 11 26 12

WITHOUT BLEMISH OR

__ __ __ __ __ __ ."
14 15 16 15 13 36

1 PETER 1:18–19

105

DOUBLE the FUN

UNSCRAMBLE THE UNDERLINED WORDS IN EACH VERSE. ON THE NEXT PAGE, PLACE YOUR ANSWERS IN THE SPACES PROVIDED AND THEN COMPLETE THE CROSSWORD PUZZLE.

1. "'THEN YOU WILL KNOW THE TRTHU, AND THE TRUTH WILL SET YOU EFER.'"

JOHN 8:32

2. "THEY ANSWERED HIM, 'WE ARE ABRAHAM'S DCESNNSAEDT AND HAVE NEVER BEEN SLAVES OF NOENAY. HOW CAN YOU SAY THAT WE SHALL BE SET FREE?'"

JOHN 8:33

3. "JESUS PRLDIEE, 'I TELL YOU THE TRUTH, YVNEOERE WHO SINS IS A SLAVE TO SIN.'"

JOHN 8:34

1. _____ _____

2. _____ _____

3. _____ _____

SCRAMBLED VERSES

UNSCRAMBLE THE WORDS BELOW AND COMPLETE THE VERSE ON THE NEXT PAGE.

"TBU ETH RTEUICSPR RCEDLASE ATTH HET OELWH DOWLR SI A NPIREROS FO NSI, OS HTTA AWTH SWA MSEDRPOI, NIBEG VGNIE RGUHOHT AHFTI NI UESJS IHRCTS, GITMH EB EINVG OT SEHOT OWH ELEBIVE."

"____ ____ _____

_____ ____ ____

_____ ____ ___ ____ ___

_____ ___ ___ ___ ,

___ ___ _____ ____

_____ , _____

_____ _____

_____ ___ ___ ___

_____ , ____ ___

_____ ___ _____

___ _____ . "

GALATIANS 3:22

109

CROSSWORD

ACROSS

1. "HE DID NOT ENTER BY _____ OF THE BLOOD OF GOATS AND CALVES."
2. "BUT HE _____ THE MOST HOLY PLACE ONCE FOR ALL."
3. "BY HIS OWN _____."
4. "_____ OBTAINED ETERNAL REDEMPTION."

DOWN

1. "HOW MUCH _____, THEN, WILL THE BLOOD OF CHRIST."
2. "WHO THROUGH THE _____ SPIRIT OFFERED HIMSELF UNBLEMISHED TO GOD."
3. "CLEANSE OUR CONSCIENCES FROM ACTS THAT LEAD TO _____."
4. "SO THAT WE MAY SERVE THE LIVING _____!"

CROSS 'EM OUT

ON THE NEXT PAGE, CROSS OUT ALL THE
LETTERS THAT APPEAR IN THE BOX FOUR
TIMES. COMPLETE THE VERSE BY PLACING
THE LETTERS THAT ARE LEFT OVER, AS THEY
APPEAR, IN THE SPACES PROVIDED.

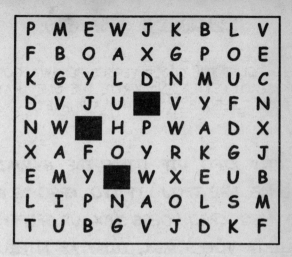

"THEREFORE, THERE IS NOW NO
CONDEMNATION FOR THOSE WHO ARE IN
___ ___ ___ ___ ___ ___ JESUS."

ROMANS 8:1

SECRET CODES

TO SOLVE THE CODED VERSES BELOW, LOOK AT EACH LETTER AND WRITE THE ONE THAT COMES BEFORE IT IN THE ALPHABET.

"CTU XIFO UIF UJNF IBE GVMMZ DPNF, HPE TFOU IJT TPO, CPSO PG B XPNBO, CPSO VOEFS MBX, UP SFEFFN UIPTF VOEFS MBX, UIBU XF NJHIU SFDFJWF UIF GVMM SJHIUT PG TPOT."

ABCDEFGHIJKLMNOPQRST UVWXYZ

"_____ _____ _____   _____

_____ _____   _____ _____

_____ _____,   _____ _____

_____ _____,   _____ _____

_____ _____,   _____

_____ _____,

_____ _____   _____

_____ _____,   _____

_____ _____   _____

_____ _____   _____

_____ _____."

GALATIANS 4:4–5

SCRAMBLED CIRCLES

ON THE NEXT PAGE, UNSCRAMBLE THE WORDS IN THE LIST BELOW. THEN USE THE CIRCLED LETTERS TO COMPLETE THE VERSE.

1. RETSAH

2. ALSLC

3. NTSAD

4. EEREICV

5. REFE

6. PITRIS

7. ULYLF

1. _ _ _ _ _ _ ◯

2. _ _ ◯ _ _ _

3. _ _ ◯ _ _

4. _ _ _ _ _ ◯ _

5. _ _ ◯ _

6. _ _ _ ◯ _ _

7. _ _ _ _ ◯

"IT IS FOR FREEDOM THAT CHRIST HAS SET US FREE. STAND FIRM, THEN, AND DO NOT LET YOURSELVES BE BURDENED AGAIN BY A YOKE OF _ _ _ _ _ _ _."

GALATIANS 5:1

ASK YOURSELF

WHAT HAVE YOU LEARNED SO FAR? FIND OUT
BY ANSWERING THE QUESTIONS BELOW.

1. WHAT DID JESUS REDEEM US
FROM?

GALATIANS 3:13-14

_____

2. HOW DID HE REDEEM US?

GALATIANS 3:13-14

_____

3. HOW DID CHRIST BECOME A
"CURSE?"

GALATIANS 3:13-14

_____

4. WHEN WE PUT OUR FAITH IN JESUS, WHAT DO WE RECEIVE?

GALATIANS 3:13–14

_____

5. IS THERE ANY CONDEMNATION FOR THOSE WHO ARE IN CHRIST?

ROMANS 8:1–2

_____

6. WHAT HAS THE SPIRIT OF LIFE SET US FREE FROM?

ROMANS 8:1–2

_____

COLOR *THE* PICTURE

HOPELESSNESS UNDER THE LAW

THE LAW IS TOUGH TO LIVE BY—IN FACT, IT'S *IMPOSSIBLE* TO LIVE BY!

THE LAW REQUIRES US TO BE *ABSOLUTELY* PERFECT, TO BE *ABSOLUTELY* OBEDIENT TO ALL ITS REGULATIONS. THE LAW HAS NO MERCY. IF WE BREAK JUST ONE OF THE COMMANDMENTS, THEN WE ARE GUILTY OF BREAKING THEM ALL.

THE VERY LAW THAT DEMANDED PERFECTION IS ACTUALLY RESPONSIBLE FOR STIRRING UP SIN IN US. SO LIVING UNDER THE LAW IS A NO-WIN SITUATION. THERE IS *NO HOPE* IN THE LAW!

THE LAW NOT ONLY LEADS US TO CHRIST, IT SHOWS US HOW DESPERATELY WE NEED HIM TO LIVE.

CROSS 'EM OUT

ON THE NEXT PAGE, CROSS OUT ALL THE LETTERS THAT APPEAR IN THE BOX FOUR TIMES. COMPLETE THE VERSE BY PLACING THE LETTERS THAT ARE LEFT OVER, AS THEY APPEAR, IN THE SPACES PROVIDED.

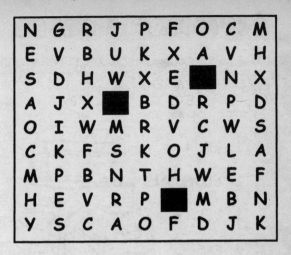

N	G	R	J	P	F	O	C	M
E	V	B	U	K	X	A	V	H
S	D	H	W	X	E	█	N	X
A	J	X	█	B	D	R	P	D
O	I	W	M	R	V	C	W	S
C	K	F	S	K	O	J	L	A
M	P	B	N	T	H	W	E	F
H	E	V	R	P	█	M	B	N
Y	S	C	A	O	F	D	J	K

"FOR WHOEVER KEEPS THE WHOLE LAW AND YET STUMBLES AT JUST ONE POINT IS __ __ __ __ __ __ OF BREAKING ALL OF IT."

JAMES 2:10

123

SCRAMBLED CIRCLES

ON THE NEXT PAGE, UNSCRAMBLE THE WORDS
IN THE LIST BELOW. THEN USE THE CIRCLED
LETTERS TO COMPLETE THE VERSE.

1. EFCA

2. ELUFLSNS

3. YELR

4. PKSEE

5. RTENTIW

6. TDNSA

1. __ __ ◯ __

2. __ ◯ __ __ __ __ __ __

3. ◯ __ __ __

4. __ __ __ __ ◯

5. __ __ __ __ __ ◯ __

6. __ __ __ __ ◯

"ALL WHO RELY ON OBSERVING THE LAW ARE UNDER A CURSE, FOR IT IS WRITTEN: '__ __ __ __ __ __ IS EVERYONE WHO DOES NOT CONTINUE TO DO EVERYTHING WRITTEN IN THE BOOK OF THE LAW.'"

GALATIANS 3:10

DOUBLE the FUN

UNSCRAMBLE THE UNDERLINED WORDS IN EACH VERSE. ON THE NEXT PAGE, PLACE YOUR ANSWERS IN THE SPACES PROVIDED AND THEN COMPLETE THE CROSSWORD PUZZLE.

1. "'YOU HAVE HEARD THAT IT WAS SAID TO THE PLPEOE LONG AGO, "DO NOT DUMRRE, AND ANYONE WHO MURDERS WILL BE EBSJTUC TO JUDGMENT."'"

MATTHEW 5:21

2. "'BUT I TELL YOU THAT NNYAEQ WHO IS ANGRY WITH HIS BROTHER WILL BE SUBJECT TO JUDGMENT. AGAIN, ANYONE WHO SAYS TO HIS BROTHER, "RACA," IS ANSWERABLE TO THE DNSIREAHN. BUT ANYONE WHO SAYS, "YOU FOOL!" WILL BE IN EANRGD OF THE FIRE OF HELL.'"

MATTHEW 5:22

1. _____ _____

_____

2. _____ _____

_____

FILL in the BLANKS

USING THE WORDS BELOW, COMPLETE THE VERSE ON THE NEXT PAGE.

WOE	GREED
INSIDE	PHARISEES
LAW	SELF-INDULGENCE
TEACHERS	CLEAN
HYPOCRITES	DISH
CUP	OUTSIDE

"'_____ TO YOU, _____

OF THE _____ AND _____,

YOU _____! YOU

_____ THE _____ OF

THE _____ AND _____,

BUT _____ THEY ARE

FULL OF _____ AND

_____.'"

CROSSWORD

ACROSS

1. "SINCE YOU DIED WITH CHRIST TO THE BASIC _____ OF THIS WORLD."
2. "WHY, AS THOUGH YOU STILL _____ TO IT."
3. "DO YOU SUBMIT TO ITS _____."
4. "'DO NOT HANDLE! DO NOT TASTE! DO NOT _____!'?"

DOWN

1. "THESE ARE ALL _____."
2. "TO _____ WITH USE."
3. "BECAUSE THEY _____ BASED."
4. "ON HUMAN COMMANDS AND _____."

ASK YOURSELF

WHAT HAVE YOU LEARNED SO FAR? FIND OUT BY ANSWERING THE QUESTIONS BELOW.

1. HOW MUCH OF THE LAW MUST BE BROKEN TO BE GUILTY OF BREAKING IT ALL?

JAMES 2:10

_____

2. HOW MUCH MUST BE KEPT TO OBEY IT ?

JAMES 2:10

_____

3. WHAT IS THE STING OF DEATH?

1 CORINTHIANS 15:56

_____

4. WHAT IS THE POWER OF SIN?

1 CORINTHIANS 15:56

_____

5. AS CHILDREN OF GOD, DO WE BELONG TO THE WORLD?

COLOSSIANS 2:20–23

_____

6. TO WHOM DO WE BELONG?

COLOSSIANS 2:20–23

_____

COLOR *the* PICTURE

THE REAL PROBLEM WITH THE LAW

THE REAL PROBLEM WITH THE LAW IS. . .YOU AND ME!

THE LAW REQUIRES US TO PERFORM, TO LIVE UP TO ITS STANDARDS. BUT BECAUSE SIN LIVES IN OUR FLESH, WE CANNOT LIVE UP TO THE LAW. WE CANNOT FREE OURSELVES FROM THE POWER OF SIN NO MATTER HOW HARD WE TRY OR HOW MUCH WE WANT TO DO GOOD. WE WILL *ALWAYS* FALL SHORT.

THE CHRISTIAN *LIFE* IS ALL ABOUT JESUS CHRIST AND NOT ABOUT US. AS LONG AS WE TRY TO LIVE UNDER THE LAW, WE MISS OUT ON THE EXPERIENCE OF JESUS LIVING *HIS LIFE* THROUGH US.

WE CAN'T DO IT—BUT *HE* CAN!

SECRET CODES

TO SOLVE THE CODED VERSES BELOW, LOOK
AT EACH LETTER AND WRITE THE ONE THAT
COMES BEFORE IT IN THE ALPHABET.

"GPS JG UIFSF IBE CFFO OPUIJOH
XSPOH XJUI UIBU GJSTU
DPWFOBOU, OP QMBDF XPVME IBWF
CFFO TPVHIU GPS BOPUIFS. CVU HPE
GPVOE GBVMU XJUI UIF QFPQMF."

A B C D E F G H I J K L M N O P Q R S T
U V W X Y Z

"_____ _____ _____ _____

_____ _____ _____

_____ _____ _____

_____, ___ _____

_____ _____ _____

_____ ___ _____.

_____ _____ _____

_____ ___ _____

_____."

HEBREWS 8:7–8

SCRAMBLED VERSES

UNSCRAMBLE THE WORDS BELOW AND COMPLETE THE VERSES ON THE NEXT PAGE.

"EW ONWK TATH HET AWL SI TRPAIISUL; TUB I MA PTLUIUAISNR, LODS SA A VSLEA OT ISN. I OD TON NSDNRDUETA AWTH I OD. RFO TAHW I NWTA OT OD I OD OTN OD, UBT WTAH I TEHA I OD. DAN FI I OD ATHW I OD ONT TANW OT OD, I EARGE ATTH ETH LWA SI ODOG. SA TI SI, TI SI ON GLEORN I EYFSML HWO OD TI, TBU TI SI NSI VGIILN NI EM."

"＿＿＿ ＿＿ ＿＿ ＿＿ ＿＿ ＿＿
＿＿ ＿＿ ＿＿ ＿＿ ；
＿＿ ＿＿ ＿＿＿＿ ，
＿＿ ＿＿ ＿＿ ＿＿
＿＿ ＿＿ ． ＿＿ ＿＿ ＿＿
＿＿ ＿＿ ＿＿ ＿＿ ＿＿
＿＿ ． ＿＿ ＿＿ ＿＿ ＿＿
＿＿ ＿＿ ＿＿ ＿＿ ＿＿
＿＿ ＿＿ ＿＿ ＿＿ ＿＿
＿＿ ． ＿＿ ＿＿ ＿＿ ＿＿
＿＿ ＿＿ ＿＿ ＿＿ ＿＿
＿＿ ＿＿ ， ＿＿ ＿＿ ＿＿
＿＿ ＿＿ ＿＿ ＿＿ ＿＿ ．
＿＿ ＿＿ ＿＿ ． ＿＿ ＿＿
＿＿ ＿＿ ＿＿ ＿＿ ＿＿
＿＿ ＿＿ ． ＿＿ ＿＿ ＿＿
＿＿ ＿＿ ＿＿ ＿＿ ＿＿ ．"

ROMANS 7:14 – 17

FINISH the VERSE

USE THE CODE CHART BELOW TO FINISH THE VERSE ON THE NEXT PAGE. (EXAMPLE: K=24)

	1	2	3	4	5	6	7
1	A	B	C	D	E	F	G
2	H	I	J	K	L	M	N
3	O	P	Q	R	S	T	U
4	V	W	X	Y	Z		

"I HAVE BEEN ___ ___ ___ ___ ___ ___ ___ ___ ___
13 34 37 13 22 16 22 15 14

WITH ___ ___ ___ ___ ___ ___ AND I NO
13 21 34 22 35 36

___ ___ ___ ___ ___ ___ LIVE, BUT CHRIST
25 31 27 17 15 34

___ ___ ___ ___ ___ IN ME. THE LIFE I
25 22 41 15 35

___ ___ ___ ___ IN THE ___ ___ ___ ___, I
25 22 41 15   12 31 14 44

LIVE BY ___ ___ ___ ___ ___ IN THE
16 11 22 36 21

___ ___ ___ OF GOD, WHO ___ ___ ___ ___ ___
35 31 27   25 31 41 15 14

ME AND GAVE ___ ___ ___ ___ ___ ___ ___
21 22 26 35 15 25 16

FOR ME."

GALATIANS 2:20

ASK YOURSELF

WHAT HAVE YOU LEARNED SO FAR? FIND OUT
BY ANSWERING THE QUESTIONS BELOW.

1. WHEN WE ARE LIVING UNDER THE
   LAW, CAN WE UNDERSTAND WHY
   WE DO WHAT WE DO?
   ROMANS 7:15–24

   _____

2. UNDER THE LAW, ARE WE ABLE TO
   DO GOOD?
   ROMANS 7:15–24

   _____

3. WHAT DO WE END UP DOING?
   ROMANS 7:15–24

   _____

4. HOW MANY TIMES ARE THE WORDS "ME, MYSELF, AND I" USED IN THIS PASSAGE?

ROMANS 7:15–24

_____

5. UNDER THE LAW, WHO IS OUR FOCUS ON?

ROMANS 7:15–24

_____

6. IF WE ARE CRUCIFIED IN CHRIST, WHO LIVES IN US?

GALATIANS 2:19–20

_____

COLOR *THE* PICTURE

YOU CAN'T MIX LAW AND GRACE

YOU CAN'T MIX LAW AND GRACE. LAW IS OUR OWN SELF-EFFORT, WHILE GRACE IS CHRIST AND HIS FINISHED WORK ON THE CROSS—IT IS *HIM* LIVING HIS LIFE THROUGH US.

HAVE YOU EVER TRIED TO MIX OIL WITH WATER? THEY DON'T BLEND TOGETHER, NO MATTER HOW MUCH YOU TRY. SO IT IS WITH LAW AND GRACE—NO MATTER HOW HARD YOU MAY TRY, YOU'LL NEVER MAKE THEM BLEND. YOU'LL ONLY END UP FRUSTRATED AND ANGRY.

GRACE *ALONE* SAVED US AND IT WILL KEEP US GOING IN OUR CHRISTIAN LIFE. WE DO THIS BY DEPENDING ON JESUS, BELIEVING BY FAITH THAT WITH ALL OUR MISTAKES AND SIN, HE CONTINUES TO LOVE US AND *ACCEPT* US TOTALLY!

CROSSWORD

ACROSS

1. "YOU FOOLISH GALATIANS! WHO HAS _____ YOU?"
2. "_____ YOUR VERY EYES."
3. "JESUS _____ WAS CLEARLY PORTRAYED AS CRUCIFIED."
4. "I WOULD LIKE TO _____ JUST ONE THING FROM YOU."

DOWN

1. "DID YOU RECEIVE THE SPIRIT BY _____ THE LAW."
2. "OR BY _____ WHAT YOU HEARD?"
3. "ARE YOU SO FOOLISH? AFTER _____ WITH THE SPIRIT."
4. "ARE YOU NOW TRYING TO ATTAIN YOUR GOAL BY _____ EFFORT?"

147

FILL in the BLANKS

USING THE WORDS BELOW, COMPLETE THE VERSES ON THE NEXT PAGE.

GOSPEL   DIFFERENT
QUICKLY   CONFUSION
ASTONISHED   GRACE
EVIDENTLY   DESERTING
TURNING   THROWING

"I AM _____ THAT YOU ARE SO _____ _____ THE ONE WHO CALLED YOU BY THE _____ OF CHRIST AND ARE _____ TO A _____ GOSPEL — WHICH IS REALLY NO GOSPEL AT ALL. _____ SOME PEOPLE ARE _____ YOU INTO _____ AND ARE TRYING TO PERVERT THE _____ OF CHRIST."

CROSS 'EM OUT

ON THE NEXT PAGE, CROSS OUT ALL THE
LETTERS THAT APPEAR IN THE BOX FOUR
TIMES. COMPLETE THE VERSE BY PLACING
THE LETTERS THAT ARE LEFT OVER, AS THEY
APPEAR, IN THE SPACES PROVIDED.

```
F Z H C I N M E J
M B Q L V A T G P
W U G P J V D U B
C E I F U B V F Z
Z V A N D Q N O T
I D L R T G U H M
G P J N K I C P A
Q Z T H B F E J L
A E L D Q M S H C
```

"AND IF BY GRACE, THEN IT IS NO
LONGER BY __ __ __ __ __; IF IT
WERE, GRACE WOULD NO LONGER BE
GRACE."

ROMANS 11:6

ASK YOURSELF

WHAT HAVE YOU LEARNED SO FAR? FIND OUT BY ANSWERING THE QUESTIONS BELOW.

1. HOW ARE WE SAVED?

ROMANS 11:6

_____

2. IF YOU TRY TO LIVE BY THE LAW AND BY GRACE, WHAT HAPPENS TO GRACE?

ROMANS 11:6

_____

3. WHAT VALUE DOES GRACE HAVE IF WE TRY BY OUR OWN EFFORT TO FIND SALVATION?

ROMANS 11:6

_____

4. ARE YOU TRYING TO LIVE AS A CHRISTIAN BY YOUR OWN SELF-EFFORT?

_____

5. AGAIN, WHAT IS THE PURPOSE OF THE LAW?

_____

6. IF YOU ARE A CHRISTIAN, WHERE DOES CHRIST LIVE?

_____

COLOR THE PICTURE

THE GRACE OF GOD

THE GRACE OF GOD IS NOT SOMETHING WE CAN EASILY DEFINE—IT'S SOMETHING WE *EXPERIENCE*.

GRACE IS THE VERY NATURE OF GOD. TRYING TO DEFINE GRACE IS LIKE TRYING TO DEFINE GOD.

UNDERSTANDING THIS GRACE IS NOT EASY. WE ALWAYS THINK THAT WITH OTHER PEOPLE WE HAVE TO DO SOMETHING OR BEHAVE IN A CERTAIN WAY TO RECEIVE THEIR LOVE AND ACCEPTANCE. WHY NOT WITH GOD?

WE CAN PRAISE GOD THAT HE IS NOT LIKE US!

GRACE IS GOD'S *GIFT* TO US, A GIFT THAT WE DO NOT NEED TO EARN. WITH GOD, WE NEED ONLY *TO BE OURSELVES!*

155

FINISH THE VERSE

USE THE CODE CHART BELOW TO FINISH THE
VERSES ON THE NEXT PAGE. (EXAMPLE: K=24)

	1	2	3	4	5	6	7
1	A	B	C	D	E	F	G
2	H	I	J	K	L	M	N
3	O	P	Q	R	S	T	U
4	V	W	X	Y	Z		

" _____ _____ _____ _____ _____ _____ _____ _____ _____ , SINCE WE
  36   21   15   34   15   16   31   34   15

HAVE BEEN _____ _____ _____ _____ _____ _____ _____ _____ _____
             23 3 7 35 36 22 16 22 15 14

THROUGH FAITH, WE HAVE

_____ _____ _____ _____ _____ WITH GOD THROUGH
 32   15   11   13   15

OUR _____ _____ _____ _____ JESUS CHRIST,
      25   31   34   14

THROUGH WHOM WE HAVE

_____ _____ _____ _____ _____ _____   _____ _____ _____ _____ _____ _____
 17 11 22 27 15 14   11 13 13 15 35 35

BY FAITH INTO THIS _____ _____ _____ _____ _____
                       17 34 11 13 15

IN WHICH WE NOW STAND. AND WE

_____ _____ _____ _____ _____ _____ _____   IN   THE
 34 15 23 31 22 13 15

_____ _____ _____ _____ OF THE _____ _____ _____ _____ _____
 21 31 32 15   17 25 31 34 44

OF GOD."

ROMANS 5:1–2

157

DOUBLE *the* FUN

UNSCRAMBLE THE UNDERLINED WORDS IN THE VERSES. ON THE NEXT PAGE, PLACE YOUR ANSWERS IN THE SPACES PROVIDED AND THEN COMPLETE THE CROSSWORD PUZZLE.

"FOR IT IS BY <u>CAGER</u> YOU HAVE <u>NEBE</u> <u>VADES</u>, THROUGH <u>IHAFT</u> — AND THIS NOT FROM <u>SOVERYUESL</u>, IT IS THE <u>FITG</u> OF GOD — NOT BY <u>RSOWK</u>, SO THAT NO ONE CAN <u>ABTOS</u>."

EPHESIANS 2:8–9

SECRET CODES

TO SOLVE THE CODED VERSES BELOW, LOOK
AT EACH LETTER AND WRITE THE ONE THAT
COMES BEFORE IT IN THE ALPHABET.

"CVU CFDBVTF PG IJT HSFBU MPWF
GPS VT, HPE, XIP JT SJDI JO NFSDZ,
NBEF VT BMJWF XJUI DISJTU
FWFO XIFO XF XFSF EFBE JO
USBOTHSFTTJPOT — JU JT CZ HSBDF
ZPV IBWF CFFO TBWFE."

ABCDEFGHIJKLMNOPQRST
UVWXYZ

"_____ _____ _____ ____

_____ _____ _____ _____

_____ ____ , _____ _____ , _____

_____ _____ _____ _____ ,

_____ _____ _____ _____

_____ _____ _____ _____

_____ _____ _____

_____ _____ _____

_ _____ _____ ____ _____ _____

_____ _____ ____ _____

_____ ."

SCRAMBLED VERSES

UNSCRAMBLE THE WORDS BELOW AND COMPLETE THE VERSES ON THE NEXT PAGE.

"NI IMH EW VEAH TERDPONIME HUHTOGR SHI ODOLB, ETH GESEIOFVSNR FO NSIS, NI NRCOAEADCC TIHW HTE EICSHR FO D'GSO EAGRC TATH EH AHDVSELI NO SU TIHW LAL OSWIDM DNA NDRUTIEAGNSND."

"_____ _____ _____ _____

_____ _____

_____ _____, _____

_____ _____,

_____ _____

_____ _____

_____ _____ _____

_____ _____ _____

_____ ."

CROSSWORD

ACROSS

1. "BUT WHEN THE KINDNESS AND LOVE OF GOD OUR SAVIOR _____."
2. "HE _____ US."
3. "NOT BECAUSE OF _____ THINGS WE HAD DONE."
4. "BUT BECAUSE OF HIS _____."

DOWN

1. "HE SAVED US THROUGH THE _____."
2. "OF REBIRTH AND _____ BY THE HOLY SPIRIT."
3. "WHOM HE POURED OUT ON US _____."
4. "THROUGH JESUS _____ OUR SAVIOR."

SCRAMBLED CIRCLES

ON THE NEXT PAGE, UNSCRAMBLE THE WORDS IN THE LIST BELOW. THEN USE THE CIRCLED LETTERS TO COMPLETE THE VERSE.

1. RFDEEOF

2. EADRGR

3. LERYFIB

4. URTE

5. NHTISG

6. TIGF

7. LULF

8. ARETNLE

1. _ _ _ ◯ _ _ _

2. _ _ _ _ ◯ _ _ _

3. _ _ ◯ _ _ _ _

4. ◯ _ _ _ _ _

5. _ ◯ _ _ _ _ _

6. _ _ ◯ _

7. _ ◯ _ _

8. _ _ _ _ _ _ ◯

"WITH THE HELP OF SILAS, WHOM I
REGARD AS A _ _ _ _ _ _ _ _ _ _
BROTHER, I HAVE WRITTEN TO YOU
BRIEFLY, ENCOURAGING YOU."

1 PETER 5:12

ASK YOURSELF

WHAT HAVE YOU LEARNED SO FAR? FIND OUT
BY ANSWERING THE QUESTIONS BELOW.

1. WHAT DO WE HAVE WITH GOD?

ROMANS 5:1–2

_____

2. WHAT DO WE NOW STAND IN?

ROMANS 5:1–2

_____

3. HOW DOES PAUL DESCRIBE THIS
   GRACE THAT SAVES US?

EPHESIANS 2:8–9

_____

4. CAN WE WORK TO EARN GOD'S GRACE?

_____

5. WHAT DID GOD DO FOR US?

EPHESIANS 2:4–5

_____

6. WHY DID GOD MAKE US ALIVE WITH CHRIST?

EPHESIANS 2:4–5

_____

ANSWER PAGES

```
H O F R L C I M T
D B T J G N Q A K
I P M V O H D P F
C R A K T E R V B
L S W H W V W G Q
P F N W L B O C I
F G V D T R A N U
K A I Q M O H P L
M C N S G B K D F
```

"FOR THE LAW WAS GIVEN THROUGH MOSES; GRACE AND TRUTH CAME THROUGH J E S U S CHRIST."

JOHN 1:17

"NOW __THEN__, WHY DO YOU TRY TO TEST __GOD__ BY __PUTTING__ ON THE __NECKS__ OF THE __DISCIPLES__ A __YOKE__ THAT NEITHER WE NOR OUR __FATHERS__ HAVE BEEN __ABLE__ TO BEAR? NO! WE __BELIEVE__ IT IS THROUGH THE __GRACE__ OF OUR LORD __JESUS__ THAT WE ARE __SAVED__, JUST AS THEY ARE."

ACTS 15:10-11

1. C A M E
2. M O S E S
3. G I V E N
4. T R Y
5. C H R I S T
6. N E C K S
7. Y O U
8. J E S U S

"SO THEN, JUST AS YOU RECEIVED CHRIST AS LORD, C O N T I N U E TO LIVE IN HIM."

COLOSSIANS 2:6

PG.13

1. __MINISTRY__   __ENGRAVED__

   __GLORY__   __STEADILY__

2. __CONDEMNS__   __MORE__

3. __FOR__   __COMPARISON__

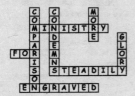

PG.15

"NOW THE __L O R D__ IS THE
25 31 34 14

__S P I R I T__, AND WHERE THE
35 32 22 31 22 36

SPIRIT OF THE LORD IS, THERE IS

__F R E E D O M__, AND WE, WHO
16 34 15 15 13 24 16

WITH UNVEILED __F A C E S__ ALL
16 11 13 15 35

__R E F L E C T__ THE LORD'S
34 15 16 15 15 13 36

__G L O R Y__   ARE   BEING
17 25 31 34 44

TRANSFORMED   INTO   HIS

__L I K E N E S S__ WITH EVER-
25 22 24 15 27 15 35 35

INCREASING   GLORY,   WHICH

__C O M E S__   FROM   THE
13 31 24 15 35

__L O R D__ WHO IS THE SPIRIT."
25 31 34 14

2 CORINTHIANS 3:17-18

PG.17

"BECAUSE OF THESE, THE __W R A T H__
OF GOD IS COMING."

COLOSSIANS 3:6

PGS.18—19

ASK YOURSELF
ANSWERS

1. THE LAW.

2. GRACE AND TRUTH.

3. A NEW COVENANT.

4. THE SPIRIT.

5. THE LETTER KILLS.

6. THE SPIRIT GIVES LIFE.

"'YOU ___YOURSELVES___ HAVE

SEEN WHAT I DID TO ___EGYPT___

AND HOW I ___CARRIED___ YOU ON

___EAGLES'___ WINGS AND

___BROUGHT___ YOU TO MYSELF.

NOW IF YOU OBEY ME ___FULLY___

AND KEEP MY ___COVENANT___. THEN

OUT OF ALL ___NATIONS___ YOU

WILL BE MY ___TREASURED___

___POSSESSION___.'"

EXODUS 19:4—5

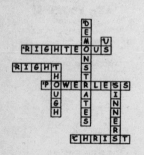

```
G M J Q H O D I P
R C F W K Z U W R
K T N Z P B J Q M
D I U (S) T R F Z W
O B H C Z G N C D
P G J Q F W J (L) O
T N F U P H (A) U T
(V) C O R M N G I B
K I (E) H D B M K Q
```

"WE KNOW THAT THE LAW IS SPIRITUAL;
BUT I AM UNSPIRITUAL, SOLD AS A
S L A V E TO SIN."

ROMANS 7:14

1. S O L <u>D</u>
2. D A R <u>E</u>
3. <u>C</u> H R I S T
4. <u>L</u> A W
5. C O V E N <u>A</u> N T
6. R A <u>R</u> E L Y
7. <u>E</u> A G L E
8. D I E <u>D</u>

"THEREFORE NO ONE WILL BE
D E C L A R E D RIGHTEOUS IN
HIS SIGHT BY OBSERVING THE LAW;
RATHER, THROUGH THE LAW WE BECOME
CONSCIOUS OF SIN."

ROMANS 3:20

"IF YOU F U L L Y OBEY THE
       16 37 25 25 44

LORD YOUR G O D AND CAREFULLY
          17 35 14

F O L L O W   ALL   HIS
16 35 25 25 35 42

C O M M A N D S I GIVE YOU
13 35 26 26 15 17 37 3

TODAY, THE L O R D YOUR GOD
           25 31 34 14

WILL SET YOU H I G H ABOVE
             11 22 17 21

ALL THE N A T I O N S ON
        27 11 36 22 31 27 35

EARTH."

DEUTERONOMY 28:1

" HOWEVER   IF   YOU

DO   NOT   OBEY   THE

LORD   YOUR   GOD   AND

DO   NOT   CAREFULLY

FOLLOW   ALL   HIS

COMMANDS   AND

DECREES   I   AM

GIVING   YOU   TODAY

ALL   THESE   CURSES

WILL   COME   UPON   YOU

AND   OVERTAKE   YOU "

DEUTERONOMY 28:15

A B C D E F G H I J K L M N O P Q R S T
U V W X Y Z

" WHAT   THEN   WAS

THE   PURPOSE   OF

THE   LAW ?   IT   WAS

ADDED   BECAUSE   OF

TRANSGRESSIONS

UNTIL   THE   SEED

TO   WHOM   THE

PROMISE   REFERRED

HAD   COME   THE   LAW

WAS   PUT   INTO

EFFECT   THROUGH

ANGELS   BY   A

MEDIATOR ."

GALATIANS 3:19

1. HOLY — COMMANDMENT
   RIGHTEOUS — GOOD
2. SPIRITUAL — UNSPIRITUAL
   SLAVE — SIN

ASK YOURSELF
ANSWERS

1. EVERYTHING THE LORD HAD SAID.

2. UNTIL THE SEED CAME.

3. JESUS CHRIST.

4. HOLY, RIGHTEOUS AND GOOD.

5. IT IS SPIRITUAL.

6. YES!

PG. 43

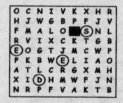

"WHAT, THEN, WAS THE PURPOSE OF THE LAW? IT WAS ADDED BECAUSE OF TRANSGRESSIONS UNTIL THE S E E D TO WHOM THE PROMISE REFERRED HAD COME."

GALATIANS 3:19

A B C D E F G H I J K L M N O P Q R S T
U V W X Y Z

" THE _____ PROMISES

_____ WERE _____ SPOKEN _____ TO

_____ ABRAHAM _____ AND _____ TO

_____ HIS _____ SEED . _____ THE

_____ SCRIPTURE _____ DOES

_____ NOT _____ SAY , _____ AND _____ TO

_____ SEEDS , _____ MEANING

_____ MANY _____ PEOPLE , _____ BUT

, _____ AND _____ TO _____ YOUR

_____ SEED , _____ MEANING

_____ ONE _____ PERSON , _____ WHO

_____ IS _____ CHRIST . "

GALATIANS 3:16

ADDED   TRESPASS

INCREASE   RIGHTEOUSNESS

ETERNAL   CHRIST

"WE KNOW THAT THE LAW IS
_____GOOD_____ IF ONE USES IT
_____PROPERLY_____ . WE ALSO KNOW
THAT _____LAW_____ IS MADE NOT FOR THE
_____RIGHTEOUS_____ BUT FOR
_____LAWBREAKERS_____ AND REBELS,
THE _____UNGODLY_____ AND
SINFUL, THE UNHOLY AND
_____IRRELIGIOUS_____ ; FOR THOSE
WHO KILL THEIR _____FATHERS_____ OR
MOTHERS, FOR MURDERERS, FOR
ADULTERERS AND PERVERTS, FOR
SLAVE _____TRADERS_____ AND LIARS
AND _____PERJURERS_____ —AND FOR
WHATEVER ELSE IS _____CONTRARY_____
TO THE SOUND _____DOCTRINE_____ . "

1 TIMOTHY 1:8—10

"T H E R E F O R E NO ONE
 36 21 15 34 15 16 31 34

WILL BE D E C L A R E D
              14 15 13 25 11 34 15 14

R I G H T E O U S IN HIS
34 22 17 21 36 15 31 37 35

SIGHT BY O B S E R V I N G
         31 12 35 15 34 41 22 27 17

THE LAW; R A T H E R ,
          34 11 36 21 15 34

THROUGH THE L A W WE BECOME
             25 11 42

C O N S C I O U S OF
13 31 27 35 13 22 31 37 35

S I N . "
35 22 27

ROMANS 3:20

175

" ___THEREFORE___ , ___JUST___ ___AS___ ___SIN___ ___ENTERED___ ___THE___ ___WORLD___ ___THROUGH___ ___ONE___ ___MAN___ ___AND___ ___DEATH___ ___THROUGH___ ___SIN___ ___AND___ ___IN___ ___THIS___ ___WAY___ ___DEATH___ ___CAME___ ___TO___ ___ALL___ ___MEN___ ___BECAUSE___ ___ALL___ ___SINNED___ — ___FOR___ ___BEFORE___ ___THE___ ___LAW___ ___WAS___ ___GIVEN___ ___SIN___ ___WAS___ ___IN___ ___THE___ ___WORLD___ ."

ROMANS 5:12-13

1. ___THEN___ ___CERTAINLY___
   ___HAVE___ ___COVETING___
2. ___SEIZING___ ___COVETOUS___
   ___DESIRE___ ___SIN___

" ___ONCE___ I WAS ___ALIVE___ ___APART___ FROM LAW; BUT WHEN THE ___COMMANDMENT___ CAME, SIN ___SPRANG___ TO ___LIFE___ AND I ___DIED___ . I ___FOUND___ THAT THE VERY COMMANDMENT THAT WAS ___INTENDED___ TO BRING ___LIFE___ ___ACTUALLY___ BROUGHT ___DEATH___ ."

ROMANS 7:9-10

ABCDEFGHIJKLMNOPQRST
UVWXYZ

" ___FOR___ ___SIN___ ___SEIZING___ ___THE___ ___OPPORTUNITY___ ___AFFORDED___ ___BY___ ___THE___ ___COMMANDMENT___ , ___DECEIVED___ ___ME___ ___AND___ ___THROUGH___ ___THE___ ___COMMANDMENT___ ___PUT___ ___ME___ ___TO___ ___DEATH___ . ___SO___ ___THEN___ , ___THE___ ___LAW___ ___IS___ ___HOLY___ , ___AND___ ___THE___ ___COMMANDMENT___ ___IS___ ___HOLY___ , ___RIGHTEOUS___ ___AND___ ___GOOD___ ."

ROMANS 7:11-12

1. R O B E
2. U T T E R L Y
3. D E C E I V E
4. G O O D
5. M E A N S
6. L I F E

"DID THAT WHICH IS GOOD, THEN,
_B E C O M E_ DEATH TO ME?
BY NO MEANS."

ROMANS 7:13

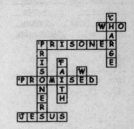

PGS.64—65

ASK YOURSELF
ANSWERS

1. IT IS A PRISONER OF SIN.

2. THROUGH FAITH IN JESUS CHRIST.

3. THOSE WHO BELIEVE.

4. THE LAW.

5. UNTIL FAITH SHOULD BE REVEALED.

6. SO THAT WE MIGHT BE JUSTIFIED BY FAITH.

1. __FORMER__ __REGULATION__
   __ASIDE__
2. __LAW__ __PERFECT__
   __BETTER__ __INTRODUCED__
   __DRAW__

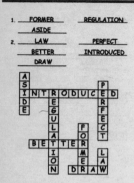

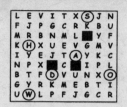

"THE LAW IS ONLY A _S_ _H_ _A_ _D_ _O_ _W_
OF THE GOOD THINGS THAT ARE COMING
—NOT THE REALITIES THEMSELVES."

HEBREWS 10:1

"FOR WHAT THE LAW WAS
_P_ _O_ _W_ _E_ _R_ _L_ _E_ _S_ _S_ TO DO IN
32 31 42 15 34 25 15 35 35
THAT IT WAS _W_ _E_ _A_ _K_ _E_ _N_ _E_ _D_
42 15 11 24 15 27 15 14
BY THE SINFUL _N_ _A_ _T_ _U_ _R_ _E_
27 11 36 37 34 15
_G_ _O_ _D_ DID BY SENDING HIS OWN
17 21 14
_S_ _O_ _N_ IN THE LIKENESS OF
35 31 27
_S_ _I_ _N_ _F_ _U_ _L_ MAN TO BE A SIN
35 22 27 14 37 25
_O_ _F_ _F_ _E_ _R_ _I_ _N_ _G_ AND SO HE
31 16 16 15 34 22 27 17
CONDEMNED _S_ _I_ _N_ IN SINFUL
35 22 27
MAN."

ROMANS 8:30

" _IS_ _THE_ _LAW_
THEREFORE _OPPOSED_
_TO_ _THE_ _PROMISES_
_OF_ _GOD_ ? _ABSOLUTELY_
NOT ! _FOR_ _IF_ _A_ _LAW_
HAD _BEEN_ _GIVEN_
THAT _COULD_ _IMPART_
LIFE _THEN_ _RIGHTEOUS_ -
NESS _WOULD_ _CERTAINLY_
HAVE _COME_ _BY_ _THE_
LAW ."

GALATIANS 3:21

178

1. J U S T I (F) I E D
2. L (A) W
3. W (I) L L
4. C H R I S (T)
5. T (H) R O U G H

"KNOW THAT A MAN IS NOT JUSTIFIED
BY OBSERVING THE LAW, BUT BY
F A I T H IN JESUS CHRIST."
GALATIANS 2:16

A B C D E F G H I J K L M N O P Q R S T
U V W X Y Z

" BUT   BECAUSE   OF
HIS   GREAT   LOVE
FOR   US   GOD   WHO
IS   RICH   IN   MERCY
MADE   US   ALIVE
WITH   CHRIST   EVEN
WHEN   WE   WERE   DEAD
IN   TRANSGRESSIONS —
IT   IS   BY   GRACE
YOU   HAVE   BEEN
SAVED   "

EPHESIANS 2:4-5

ASK YOURSELF
ANSWERS

1. IT IS SET ASIDE.

2. NO...NOT EVER.

3. BY FAITH IN JESUS CHRIST.

4. NO.

5. THE LAW BRINGS DEATH.

6. GOD.

179

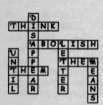

" HE SAID TO THEM
THIS IS WHAT I
TOLD YOU WHILE I
WAS STILL WITH
YOU : EVERYTHING
MUST BE FULFILLED
THAT IS WRITTEN
ABOUT ME IN THE
LAW OF MOSES
THE PROPHETS AND
THE PSALMS "

LUKE 24:44

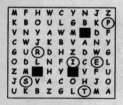

" FOR WE DO NOT HAVE A HIGH
P R I E S T WHO IS UNABLE
TO SYMPATHIZE WITH OUR
WEAKNESSES."

HEBREWS 4:15

"FOR THE W A G E S OF S I N
    42 11 17 18 35   35 22 27

IS D E A T H . BUT THE
    14 15 11 36 21

G I F T OF G O D IS
17 22 16 36   17 37 14

E T E R N A L L I F E
19 34 15 34 27 11 25   35 22 16 19

IN CHRIST J E S U S OUR
                23 15 35 37 35

L O R D ."
25 31 34 14

ROMANS 6:23

1. E T E R N **A** L
2. **G** I **F** T
3. W I T H **O** U T
4. U **N** A B L E
5. P R I **E** S T
6. S I **N**
7. W A **G** E S

"HE IS THE **A T O N I N G** SACRIFICE FOR OUR SINS, AND NOT ONLY FOR OURS BUT ALSO FOR THE SINS OF THE WHOLE WORLD."

1 JOHN 2:2

"WHEN YOU WERE __DEAD__ IN YOUR __SINS__ AND IN THE __UNCIRCUMCISION__ OF YOUR SINFUL __NATURE__, GOD MADE YOU ALIVE WITH CHRIST. HE __FORGAVE__ US ALL OUR SINS, HAVING CANCELED THE __WRITTEN__ CODE, WITH ITS __REGULATIONS__ THAT WAS AGAINST US AND THAT STOOD __OPPOSED__ TO US: HE TOOK IT AWAY, __NAILING__ IT TO THE __CROSS__."

COLOSSIANS 2:13–14

1. POWERLESS   WEAKENED
   SENDING   SINFUL
2. CONDEMNED   DO
   LIVE   SPIRIT

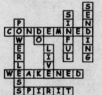

ASK YOURSELF
ANSWERS

1. TO FUFILL IT.

2. HE WOULD.

3. HE CANCELLED IT.

4. HE NAILED IT TO THE CROSS.

5. ON THE CROSS.

6. NO!

" ___CHRIST___ ___REDEEMED___ US FROM THE ___CURSE___ OF THE ___LAW___ BY ___BECOMING___ A CURSE FOR US, FOR IT IS ___WRITTEN___ : ' ___CURSED___ IS ___EVERYONE___ WHO IS ___HUNG___ ON A ___TREE___ .' "

GALATIANS 3:13

"FOR YOU <u>K N O W</u> THAT
         24 27 31 42
IT WAS NOT WITH
<u>P E R I S H A B L E</u>
32 18 34 22 35 11 12 25 18
THINGS SUCH AS <u>S I L V E R</u>
          35 12 23 15 18 34
OR <u>G O L D</u> THAT YOU WERE
  17 31 23 14
REDEEMED FROM THE <u>E M P T Y</u>
              18 32 32 31 44
WAY OF <u>L I F E</u> HANDED DOWN
     23 22 16 18
TO YOU FROM YOUR
<u>F O R E F A T H E R S</u>,
16 31 34 18 16 11 36 22 18 34 35
BUT WITH THE <u>P R E C I O U S</u>
            32 34 18 37 22 31 37 35
BLOOD OF CHRIST, A <u>L A M B</u>
                23 11 32 12
WITHOUT BLEMISH OR
<u>D E F E C T</u>."
14 18 16 18 37 36

1 PETER 1:18-19

1. ___TRUTH___ ___FREE___
2. ___DESCENDANTS___ ___ANYONE___
3. ___REPLIED___ ___EVERYONE___

" BUT THE SCRIPTURE
DECLARES THAT THE
WHOLE WORLD IS A
PRISONER OF SIN
SO THAT WHAT WAS
PROMISED , BEING
GIVEN THROUGH
FAITH IN JESUS
CHRIST , MIGHT BE
GIVEN TO THOSE
WHO BELIEVE ."

GALATIANS 3:22

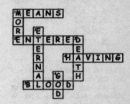

"THEREFORE, THERE IS NOW NO
CONDEMNATION FOR THOSE WHO ARE IN
C H R I S T JESUS."

ROMANS 8:1

ABCDEFGHIJKLMNOPQRST
UVWXYZ

" BUT WHEN THE
TIME HAD FULLY
COME GOD SENT
HIS SON BORN OF
A WOMAN , BORN
UNDER LAW TO
REDEEM THOSE
UNDER LAW , THAT
WE MIGHT RECEIVE
THE FULL RIGHTS
OF SONS ."

GALATIANS 4:4-5

1. H E A R T (S)
2. C A L L S
3. S T A N D
4. R E C E I (V) E
5. F R E (E)
6. S P (I) R I T
7. F U L L (Y)

"IT IS FOR FREEDOM THAT CHRIST HAS SET US FREE. STAND FIRM, THEN, AND DO NOT LET YOURSELVES BE BURDENED AGAIN BY A YOKE OF S L A V E R Y."

GALATIANS 5:1

ASK YOURSELF
ANSWERS

1. THE CURSE OF THE LAW.

2. HE BECAME A CURSE FOR US.

3. HE WAS "HUNG ON A TREE."

4. THE PROMISE OF THE SPIRIT.

5. NO.

6. THE LAW OF SIN AND DEATH.

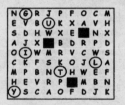

```
N (G) R J P F O C M
E V B (U) K X A V H
S D H W X E   N X
A J X   B D R P D
O (I) W M R V C W S
C K F S K O J (L) A
M P B N (T) H W E F
H E V R P   M B N
(Y) S C A O F D J K
```

"FOR WHOEVER KEEPS THE WHOLE LAW AND YET STUMBLES AT JUST ONE POINT IS G U I L T Y OF BREAKING ALL OF IT."

JAMES 2:10

PG.125

1. F A **C** E
2. F **U** L L N E S S
3. **R** E L Y
4. K E E P **S**
5. W R I T T **E** N
6. S T A N **D**

"ALL WHO RELY ON OBSERVING THE LAW ARE UNDER A CURSE, FOR IT IS WRITTEN: '**C U R S E D** IS EVERYONE WHO DOES NOT CONTINUE TO DO EVERYTHING WRITTEN IN THE BOOK OF THE LAW.'"

GALATIANS 3:10

PG.127

1.   PEOPLE   MURDER

   SUBJECT

2.   ANYONE   SANHEDRIN

   DANGER

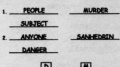

PG.129

" _WOE_ TO YOU, _TEACHERS_ OF THE _LAW_ AND _PHARISEES_ YOU _HYPOCRITES_ ! YOU _CLEAN_ THE _OUTSIDE_ OF THE _CUP_ AND _DISH_ BUT _INSIDE_ THEY ARE FULL OF _GREED_ AND _SELF-INDULGENCE_ ."

MATTHEW 23:25

PG.131

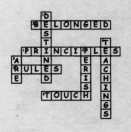

185

ASK YOURSELF
ANSWERS

1. JUST ONE PART.

2. THE WHOLE LAW.

3. SIN.

4. THE POWER OF SIN IS THE LAW.

5. NO.

6. TO CHRIST.

PG. 137

ABCDEFGHIJKLMNOPQRST
UVWXYZ

" FOR IF THERE HAD BEEN NOTHING WRONG WITH THAT FIRST COVENANT NO PLACE WOULD HAVE BEEN SOUGHT FOR ANOTHER BUT GOD FOUND FAULT WITH THE PEOPLE . "

HEBREWS 8:7—8

PG. 139

" WE KNOW THAT THE LAW IS SPIRITUAL ; BUT I AM UNSPIRITUAL , SOLD AS A SLAVE TO SIN . I DO NOT UNDERSTAND WHAT I DO . FOR WHAT I WANT TO DO I DO NOT DO BUT WHAT I HATE I DO . AND IF I DO WHAT I DO NOT WANT TO DO , I AGREE THAT THE LAW IS GOOD . AS IT IS , IT IS NO LONGER I MYSELF WHO DO IT , BUT IT IS SIN LIVING IN ME . "

ROMANS 7:14—17

"I HAVE BEEN C R U C I F I E D
13 34 27 13 22 16 22 15 14

WITH C H R I S T AND I NO
13 21 34 22 35 36

L O N G E R LIVE, BUT CHRIST
25 31 27 17 15 14

L I V E S IN ME. THE LIFE I
25 22 41 15 35

L I V E IN THE B O D Y I
25 22 41 15 12 31 14 44

LIVE BY F A I T H IN THE
16 11 22 36 21

S O N OF GOD, WHO L O V E D
35 31 27 25 31 41 15 14

ME AND GAVE H I M S E L F
21 22 21 15 25 16

FOR ME."

GALATIANS 2:20

ASK YOURSELF
ANSWERS

1. NO.

2. NO.

3. WHAT WE DO NOT WANT TO DO.

4. THIRTY-ONE TIMES.

5. ME, MYSELF, AND I.

6. CHRIST LIVES IN US.

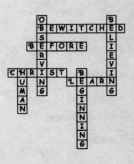

"I AM _____ASTONISHED_____ THAT YOU ARE SO _____QUICKLY_____ _____DESERTING_____ THE ONE WHO CALLED YOU BY THE _____GRACE_____ OF CHRIST AND ARE _____TURNING_____ TO A _____DIFFERENT_____ GOSPEL — WHICH IS REALLY NO GOSPEL AT ALL. _____EVIDENTLY_____ SOME PEOPLE ARE _____THROWING_____ YOU INTO _____CONFUSION_____ AND ARE TRYING TO PERVERT THE _____GOSPEL_____ OF CHRIST."

GALATIANS 1:6—7

```
F Z H C I N M E J
M B Q L V A T G P
(W) U G P J V D U B
C E I F U B V F Z
Z V A N D Q N (O) T
I D L (R) T G U H M
G P J N (K) I C P A
Q Z T H B F E J L
A E L D Q M (S) H C
```

"AND IF BY GRACE, THEN IT IS NO LONGER BY _W_O_R_K_S_; IF IT WERE, GRACE WOULD NO LONGER BE GRACE."

ROMANS 11:6

PGS.152—153

ASK YOURSELF
ANSWERS

1. BY GRACE ALONE!

2. GRACE COULD NOT BE GRACE.

3. NO VALUE AT ALL.

4. LET'S HOPE NOT!

5. TO LEAD US TO CHRIST.

6. IN ME.

"T H E R E F O R E, SINCE WE
24 21 24 31 34 15

HAVE BEEN J U S T I F I E D
32 15 4 21 22 14 22 18 14

THROUGH FAITH, WE HAVE

P E A C E WITH GOD THROUGH
12 15 4 23 15

OUR L O R D JESUS CHRIST,
25 21 34 14

THROUGH WHOM WE HAVE

G A I N E D   A C C E S S
17 4 22 27 15 14   4 23 23 15 26 26

BY FAITH INTO THIS G R A C E
17 34 4 23 15

IN WHICH WE NOW STAND. AND WE

R E J O I C E   IN   THE
34 15 31 21 22 23 15

H O P E OF THE G L O R Y
21 21 12 15   17 25 21 34 44

OF GOD."

ROMANS 5:1-2

GRACE   BEEN

SAVED   FAITH

YOURSELVES   GIFT

WORKS   BOAST

ABCDEFGHIJKLMNOPQRST
UVWXYZ

" BUT   BECAUSE   OF

HIS   GREAT   LOVE

FOR   US   GOD   WHO

IS   RICH   IN   MERCY

MADE   US   ALIVE

WITH   CHRIST   EVEN

WHEN   WE   WERE   DEAD

IN   TRANSGRESSIONS

- IT   IS   BY   GRACE

YOU   HAVE   BEEN

SAVED ."

EPHESIANS 2:4-5

" IN   HIM   WE   HAVE

REDEMPTION   THROUGH

HIS   BLOOD   THE

FORGIVENESS   OF   SINS

IN   ACCORDANCE

WITH   THE   RICHES

OF   GOD'S   GRACE

THAT   HE   LAVISHED

ON   US   WITH

ALL   WISDOM   AND

UNDERSTANDING ."

EPHESIANS 1:7-8

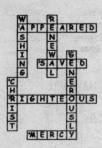

1. O F F E R E D
2. R E G A R D
3. B R I E F L Y
4. T R U E
5. T H I N G S
6. G I F T
7. F U L L
8. E T E R N A L

"WITH THE HELP OF SILAS, WHOM I REGARD AS A F A I T H F U L BROTHER, I HAVE WRITTEN TO YOU BRIEFLY, ENCOURAGING YOU."

1 PETER 5:12

PGS.168—169

ASK YOURSELF
ANSWERS

1. PEACE WITH GOD.

2. GRACE.

3. IT IS A GIFT OF GOD.

4. NO!

5. MADE US ALIVE WITH CHRIST.

6. BECAUSE OF HIS GREAT LOVE FOR US.

SUPER BIBLE ACTIVITIES FOR KIDS!

Barbour's Super Bible Activity Books, packed with fun illustrations and kid-friendly text, will appeal to children ages six to twelve. And the price—only $1.39—will appeal to parents. All books are paperbound. The unique size (4¹⁄₈" x 5³⁄₈") makes these books easy to take anywhere!

A Great Selection to Satisfy All Kids!

Bible Activities
Bible Activities for Kids
Bible Connect the Dots
Bible Crosswords for Kids
Bible Picture Fun
Bible Word Games
Bible Word Searches for Kids
Clean Jokes for Kids
Fun Bible Trivia

Fun Bible Trivia 2
Great Bible Trivia for Kids
More Bible Activities
More Bible Crosswords for Kids
More Clean Jokes for Kids
Super Bible Activities
Super Bible Crosswords
Super Bible Word Searches
Super Silly Stories